THE ARCHANGEL OF
WESTMINSTER

By

Michael Shaughnessy

ISBN: 1-4107-3430-7 (e-book)
ISBN: 1-4107-3429-3 (Paperback)

This book is printed on acid free paper.

1stBooks - rev. 03/17/03

CONTENTS

ACKNOWLEDGEMENTS

The Servants of the Word, the ecumenical brotherhood of which I am a member, is something only God could put (and keep) together. Someday a history will be written recounting how we went from praying on our own to praying together in our "prayer rooms". We had run out of individual "prayer closets" and needed a solution, so we just all piled into one room and made *a joyful noise to the Lord* together. We have since grown in our understanding and appreciation of liturgy, form, order, and ambience.

However, I still remember when 710 Catherine Street, Ann Arbor, Michigan, had a dirt floor in the basement, with wood thrown down across it and old carpet laid out to cover the wood. The lighting was terrible, the musty smell uninviting and yet literally hundreds of (now not so) young men remember that prayer room, probably because God joined us every morning as we worshipped.

It was in one of these prayer rooms that the inspiration for writing this book first came. It is described in the book so I'll let that suffice.

The book itself has been an on again off again affair during my holidays and days off. Several people helped me by reading it along the way and kicking me for not publishing it, including Bob Bell, Alex Perry, and Maureen Robinson. At least as worthy of mention are the many who knew I was writing it and constantly asked when it would be finished. The financial help of the Bread of Life Community finally got me ready to do something, like have it proof read. Seeing my first

v

work in print, the *Concise Catholic Catechism*, helped with finishing this as well.

My real thanks must begin with the source of faith, life and truth: first, last and only God. However, he chose to use much in his creation to convince me of his truth. In my case he used my family, especially my father, GT and mother Jackie. My brother and sisters, Kelly, Carmen, Shannon and Colleen all helped in the process as well, simply by being part of the environment of faith that characterised our family.

In my high school years the work of the Young Life organisation also had a significant impact on me, bringing my Catholic roots "life above ground".

My other great debt is to the Servants of the Word. The wonderful cross-pollination of Protestants and Catholics, the international mix of brothers, the unbelievable variety of personalities and the non-stop creativity of them all has certainly affected me, and my faith.

Michael Shaughnessy
The Feast of the Incarnation 2003

PREFACE

A child is easily convinced that unusual beings inhabit the earth. Angels and demons, leprechauns and ghosts were as real to me as a child as dogs and rabbits. My imagination was alive. My fantasy world of fairies and dragons was just as real as my ordinary world of school and neighbourhood. They seemed to operate on two different sets of principles, but neither seemed less plausible than the other. My understanding was woefully inadequate.

As I grew older I made an all too common error. Instead of dismissing an inadequate understanding of spirits, I threw out the spirits altogether. I threw out the demon along with the pitchfork. (The pitchfork won't return to bother you, but the demon will.)

Still, most adults at least suspect there are angels, both good and evil, dwelling among us but that these angels remain unseen—for the most part that is.

The problem facing any adult, who happens to see an angel, is deciding whether or not to admit it. He or she will face an audience, most of whom believe in angels. Many of whom would even believe that seeing an angel is possible—although improbable. Because it is improbable, nearly everyone dismisses any account of seeing an angel as either a mild case of insanity or a momentary loss of consciousness. The improbable often is treated like the impossible.

So, what about me and what about the story I have written? Well, as far as I know, I have never seen an angel, but I believe they exist and act more or less as described in the story.

Kate's story is true in all its basic details, although the names and minor details have been changed. I also actually had the vision described in chapter one. Much of the rest is simply a product of reflection on the New Testament and fantasy.

The reader will not find it easy to distinguish exactly where fact ends and fantasy begins. It is not intended to be easy. Nor is it possible.

The definitive understanding of the interaction of angels and human beings will only be available in the next world. That will be far more interesting than the best of what follows.

CHAPTER 1:

THE FIRST VISITATION

She entered "the tube" and sat across from me on the District Line—the London Underground route marked in green on the map. She was young, dressed in black from head to toe and a walking pin cushion—five rings in each ear, three through her left eyebrow, two through her right nostril, another two through her upper lip and who knows how many others or where. "I'm back in London," I thought to myself. I never expected to see her once I left the train. I was wrong. But then I never expected to interview an angel either.

Turnham Green, Stamford Brook, Ravenscourt Park, Hammersmith; station after station passed, the platforms crowded with people determined to reach their destination and fulfil their purpose—except possibly her. She seemed completely out of place, evidencing no sense of purpose or destination. Why would any woman wear black army boots? I guess I am showing my age.

My eye wandered around the carriage. Those standing by the doors on the train rocked back and forth holding onto whatever was available. Suddenly, the daylight disappeared as we passed into an underground tunnel. The noise of the train doubled. At the next station the doors again opened with a hydraulic pssshhhh. A bored voice announced, "Mind the gap," reminding travellers not to misstep and fall onto the track. People hurried through the doors. One bumped into another, "Sorry." The batteries underneath the carriage whined as they recharged. "Mind the doors, please, mind the doors," preceded another hydraulic psssshhhh and the doors closed.

"She could be a very attractive young lady if she wanted to be," I thought. My eye had again settled back into its natural place looking forward. "To each his own...or her own, I guess."

I looked up at the advertisements posted along the inside of this underground python. Cigarettes and success, houses and hotels, lagers, bitters, ales, and stout; each commanding your eye "look at me." My hungry eye flitted from one to another until it was saturated with colours, words, and shapes. Their power to hold my attention waned and again I looked back at the young woman and wondered about her life. "What do you do all day? Is it worthwhile? Is it even interesting? Why? Where are you going?"

My destination, like many of the people seated in my carriage was Victoria Station. As things turned out, it was hers, too.

Only those inexperienced with the underground look around. The regulars don't. They don't need to. They step out through the sliding doors onto the platform, turn and walk to the "Way Out." Tourists and other novices like me stick out. I minded the gap, stepped onto the platform and stopped, looking for the "Way Out" sign. Ten people walked past me, all of them moving from left to right. Twice I was in the way of someone and got bumped.

"Sorry."

"Excuse me," I responded, as any misplaced American tourist would.

I finally noticed the "Way Out" sign pointing in the direction everyone was moving, to the right, so I finally fell in step and proceeded to the end of the platform, down a corridor and out into an open area with signs and arrows: "Victoria Line North, Victoria Line South, Victoria Station, Way Out." Again I stopped and looked while everyone hurried past me.

"What will I face at the gate," I wonder, "a man in a small ticket booth?" No, here it is a machine with a picture of a ticket and the words "insert here."

"Will it eat my ticket?" I wondered. "It's a return ticket. I need it to get back home. Which pocket did I put it in?" Not having developed habitual behaviour regarding underground tickets yet, I began a mental body search, but it wasn't necessary. I had kept it in my hand. I didn't want to lose it.

Into the slot it went, whisked from my fingers and spat back out the top. The machine affirmed my honesty, opened the gates and let me pass. Another barrier conquered, my confidence increased, I set out to find Westminster Cathedral. Fortunately it is only two hundred yards from the front of the station according to the A to Z map of London.

"Kate! Kate!" A well-dressed, professional looking young lady was waving on tiptoe to the young woman in black.

"Fiona?" She responded with little enthusiasm.

I was intrigued by the study in contrast. What could those two have in common? But then remembered I was trying to get to Westminster

Cathedral. I looked again at my map and located the cathedral and its proximity to Victoria Station. Only then did I realise I had no idea exactly where I was in Victoria Station. The "Way Out" signs, which I had faithfully followed, did not distinguish between the front, the sides and the rear of the station. Having learned something earlier about crowd flow—it normally is heaviest in the direction you are supposed to go—I went with the flow and found my self at the front of the building, needing to cross Wilton Road and Vauxhall Bridge Road. Confident now about where I was and which direction I was to go, I again ignored the crowds and got on with my task. Faithful to my upbringing I looked to my left, saw no oncoming traffic, and stepped onto the road. Fortunately the taxi had good brakes. It also had a good horn.

I remembered the well-known and often forgotten fact. Vehicles drive on the left in Britain. Pedestrians are supposed to look to the right. The cab driver glowered at me, caught my eye, and then gazed at my feet. I backed onto the curb again and looked down at the pavement. Written there, in white twelve inch letters were the words: "LOOK RIGHT." It wasn't an advertisement for a clothing shop.

I had come to London because I work for a travel company. I was to put together a tour for the coming summer's tourist season. I started by reviewing all the popular sights—Madame Tussaud's, Buckingham Palace, the Tower of London, Windsor Castle—and was now heading back into the heart of London to review some other sights. Like any tourist I was getting satiated with sights and facts I would quickly forget like a lunch at a McDonald's in Minneapolis—or was it Detroit?

Westminster Cathedral is set back off Victoria Street. As I turned past the last building—which happens to be yet another McDonalds, I gasped. The building didn't look right. Like many tourists, I confused Westminster Abbey and Westminster Cathedral. "Better make note of that." I thought, continuing with: "I might as well take a quick look."

Westminster Cathedral is made of twelve and one half million hand-made bricks. It is 360 feet long, 156 wide and 117 to the top of the nave. Tourism books are full of these kinds of facts that are difficult to remember and useless as well. Which means that I will put them into my tourism brochure for Westminster Cathedral. The front of the building is adorned with the usual abundance of statues, gargoyles, and stained glass windows. Two statues representing the Archangels Michael and Gabriel are posted above the doors. I stepped inside.

The cathedral was busy. Suddenly, I remembered it was Wednesday of Holy Week. The line for confession was long. Tourists were gawking and taking pictures of things they can buy in the card shop cheaper than the photos they take themselves. Other people were quietly praying. The floor in the nave was being waxed. Extra chairs were being set up for anticipated over-flow crowds expected on Maundy Thursday and Good Friday. A man on my left was dusting a statue of St. Peter. There was a smell of wood polish in the air. Everything around me was being prepared in anticipation of the great feast of Easter.

I walked to the racks holding guides, magazines and bulletins. I wanted a guide to the building. Near one of the racks a man was standing alone. He seemed to be reading to himself. "Don't miss the Chapel of St. Michael the Archangel. In front of the altar you will see St. Michael the warrior as he appears..." and his voice trailed off as he turned the page. Since my name is Michael, I decided I would make a point of seeing the chapel. The man's quiet voice continued, "The chapel is located in the front of the cathedral on the left." Then he turned away and was off, apparently to go on his own brochure-guided tour.

I put a pound into the moneybox, picked up a guide and began making my way through the long aisles of the cathedral, reading as I went. Like almost every cathedral, the lighting was dim and the temperature cool.

"Not a very impressive set of tombs," I thought to myself as I went along. I had recently been to Windsor Castle and seen the burial crypts of numerous kings and queens, knights and nobles: Henrys and Marys, Williams and Edwards. "But then, this church isn't really all that old. Too bad. I had hoped this would be more interesting."

I passed the chapels of All Souls, St. George, and St. Joseph, noticing my footfalls echo of off the marble walls of the nave. It all gave a sense of majesty and importance.

As I reached the front of the cathedral on the left, I was consoling myself with the thought of seeing the statue of "St. Michael the Warrior". I expected something twelve to fifteen feet tall that captured both the fierceness of a warrior and the holiness of an angel.

I looked around the chapel for the statue. Finally, I saw it. It was two feet tall, and done in low relief on the front of the altar. I was not impressed. None-the-less, I stepped up to the altar and bent down to get a closer look.

Someone approached from the rear as I continued my observation. A quiet, masculine voice spoke, "It's not a bad work of art." I turned around to look. As I did, he said, "I believe it was you that requested the interview."

I straightened back up. "Excuse me?" I couldn't recall any request for an interview and I certainly couldn't place this man's face. It was vaguely familiar. He was about six feet tall with tightly curled blond hair. Most noticeable were his eyes. The iris was light blue, in a starred pattern. The corona was a dark blue, almost navy.

The stranger repeated his question. "I believe it was you that requested an interview. 12 months ago. I'm sorry I have taken so long in reaching you, but I have been quite busy."

"This is London," I thought, remembering the young woman with all the rings. I said, "Sorry, I think you are looking for someone else."

He ignored what I said and continued. "You were in Ann Arbor, Michigan, last year, one week before Good Friday."

I quickly checked to make sure I wasn't wearing something that said Michigan or Ann Arbor on it. I wasn't.

"You said," he continued, "'I wonder what it would be like to see an angel.'" He paused and looked again at the statue of Michael the Archangel. "No, not a bad work of art, but it doesn't really capture who I am."

"Yup, another whacko." I thought, but then I shuddered thinking, "Maybe he has been following me. Could be a pick-pocket." I needed to decide what to do. A quick exit from the cathedral seemed to make the most sense. I stood to go. He continued to look at the statue and carried on speaking.

"It was eight in the morning. You were singing the song 'Oh Sacred Head Surrounded.' Once you got to the line, 'And angel hosts adored thee and trembled as they gazed,' you saw in your mind a vision of an angel trembling before the cross as Christ was crucified. That was when you said, 'I wonder what it would be like to see an angel…better yet, I would like to speak to one that was there.' Your request has been granted. Do you still want the interview?"

My memory became suddenly and awkwardly clear. His description was accurate to the smallest detail, although the thought to speak to an angel was a fleeting one. I had later tossed the idea around with a few friends, but that was it.

My mind was thrashing the data. What to do now? I finally came up with a question rather than an answer, "Well, is this man an angel or isn't he?" I knew that was the right question, but you don't just ask someone, 'So, are you really an angel?'

"So, are you really an angel?" I asked.

"Yes." he answered, "I am Michael the Archangel."

I looked at him and then, again, at the statue. There was little resemblance.

"It lacks a sense of purpose and determination." He said.

I looked again at him. From head to foot he was a very ordinary man in most respects. I was about to leave when I heard myself say: "You don't look much like an angel."

"Oh?"

"No."

"And how many have you seen?"

"Ah...Well, I really haven't ever seen one. At least, not a real one."

"You have, actually. You have seen two. With the first you didn't know it, and with the second you don't believe it...at least not yet."

He saw my puzzled look.

"When you entered the cathedral I believe you were directed here by a man saying, 'don't miss the Chapel of St. Michael the Archangel. Near the altar you will see St. Michael the warrior as he appears. The chapel is located in the front of the cathedral on the left.'"

I looked away trying to collect my thoughts. How could this man know these facts? The man at the entrance to the cathedral had been whispering. There was no one else near us.

"Is that what it says in the guide-book?" He continued.

I opened the guide to page 18 and read under the words: The Chapel of St. Michael. "On the frontal is a low relief of St. Michael." That was all there was. No exhortation: "Don't miss." No reference to a warrior.

"That angel was giving you orders, not reading from a guide book."

I began to fear that London was having its effect on me more than on him. I mentally made a note to check the yellow pages for a psychiatrist.

"Look at me." He said softly, but with authority. I looked at him.

"I am Michael. My name means 'the right hand of God,' or 'he who is like God,' and I am an archangel."

The authority in his voice was suddenly amazing, like the authority of irrefutable truth. I began to doubt my doubt. I noticed I was becoming very self-conscious, aware of my own smallness, and this person's greatness. I felt compelled to kneel and fought it.

It was if he read my mind. He took me by the elbow and held me up. "Do not kneel. I am an angel, a servant of the Most High, but you are right to be in awe, for I hold the highest rank in the army of heaven."

Now my doubt vanished. It was replaced by fear and an odd certitude that this was indeed an Archangel.

"I am a warrior." He continued. "My orders come directly from the Most High himself. My master is at war and I am at war in this, an unprecedented age of warfare. The powers of spiritual darkness have gained greater and greater influence in the affairs of the world, conspiring together against the Lord and the race made in his image and likeness. At issue is the eternal fate of every individual. These are days destined for battle, a battle for the soul of every human being. In this we, the host of heaven, are engaged day and night, in every nation, in every city and every home. There is not a man, woman or child whom we do not defend. Indeed, we are nearing the day of the great battle when the Lord's anointed will stun the enemy and bring him to his knees. In that day, once and for all, humanity will be free from the trial of temptation, from the disfigurement of sin, from the tyranny of death. In that day the power of Satan will be broken and every knee shall bend and every tongue confess that Jesus Christ is Lord of all, including Satan himself."

Michael continued in a softer yet still authoritative voice, "The vision you had of the angel before the cross was more accurate than you might have thought. My perspective on that day is a story meant to be written, and you must write it. I will answer your questions so that you can do it."

"What story? For whom?" I thought, though I expected it would become clear in time. "So, when should I start to ask questions?"

"You have already asked five questions,…seven if you include the original requests for an interview, and thirteen if you include the ones you have thought but not asked."

It was suddenly becoming clear to me that my mind was an open book to him. I wondered how to proceed. "Is what I am thinking that obvious?" I asked.

"To me, yes."

I didn't know what to do. None of my training in the tourism industry exactly prepared me for interviewing an archangel. Personal questions flooded into my mind: "do you know about that time I lied to my boss? Are my parents in heaven?" I resisted these questions and decided to conduct the interview in as professional a manner as possible.

"How long will I have with you?" I asked.

"I don't know," Michael replied. "I haven't been told, but I am sure it will be long enough to tell you what is necessary."

His response helped. I felt I could speak to him as I would to a normal person, not as an unapproachable being of tremendous glory who could destroy me with a flick of his finger. "Well, that will take the pressure off to rush through this." I responded. "Next question…Are you visible?"

"Can you see me?"

"Yes."

"Well?"

"What I mean is, can other people see you?"

"Yes, I am as visible as you are."

"What if someone I know sees me and begins to talk to us?"

"Yes?"

"I assume you don't want everyone around here to know you are an angel do you?"

"No, you are right, but how would they know?"

"What if I told them? What would you do, disappear?"

"Oh, quite the contrary. I'd just stand here and look at you." I saw his point: Who would believe me if I said, "Hey folks, do you realise you are looking at Michael the Archangel?"

"A nut-case. Totally bonkers that one!" I could read their thoughts already. How could I convince anyone? I would simply end up rather embarrassed. I asked my next question.

"Are there other angels around here now?"

"Many."

"Where? Are they visible?"

"No, not just now. In fact, most of us never take visible shape. But to answer your first question in a bit more detail, this building is filled with them. As you can see, there are quite a few tourists here as well as some who are here to pray. Wherever there are people, there are angels as well."

"What do they all do?"

"It depends on what type of angels they are, and their level of rank. We are quite diverse in what we do, how we appear, how we work, and what powers we have."

"Could you explain? You said angels are divided according to their rank…"

"Yes, each of us is given a rank, and with our rank come certain powers and privileges. It works a lot like your military ranking systems. Some of us are like generals and captains, colonels and sergeants, although we use different terms. I am sure you are at least familiar with some of them: angels, archangels, cherubim and seraphim. Those of us of higher rank have greater power. We can intervene in the course of nature—only in obedience, of course. Whereas some of those of lower rank can only sow ideas or thoughts in the mind."

"You said there were different types of work in which you are engaged. What are they?"

"There are angels who act primarily as messengers. They bring revelation from the Most High to human hearts and minds. They give pastors inspiration for sermons and musicians ideas for hymns. It was one of these that gave you the vision twelve months ago.

I was a bit surprised by this. I thought it had just been an idea that had occurred to me, but no, apparently angels were more involved in my life than I had thought. I shook off the distraction.

I was sure I could guess what the warriors did, so I asked about the angels of comfort.

"Angels of comfort...They have a great role to play for those who are lonely or in misery, whether that is due to sin or simply the circumstances of their life. With the great amount of suffering in the world today we have assigned many to this role. Every victim of war, famine, illness, and disaster is assigned an angel of comfort. This is true even when the misery is due to sin. Each person in these circumstances is assigned an angel to comfort them and draw them back to the truth. The greatest of sinners still receives the offer of comfort from the Most High even if they do not want it. These angels minister by urging the individuals assigned to them to cry out to the Most High for mercy. The Most High, in his great love, is always ready to show it. He wants them restored. Whenever someone cries out to him for help they receive it. Unfortunately, many are so hard of heart that even in the greatest of misery they refuse his mercy...But when the least of them turn to him, the rejoicing in heaven is great."

"Is the rejoicing done by these angels of comfort or by some others?"

"Well actually, by both. Certainly those involved rejoice, but also the angels of worship. They are the ones described in the Book of Revelation, those who never leave the throne room in heaven and never cease to praise the Most High. Before the fall of Satan we were all angels of worship."

The fall of Satan—I knew my next question.

CHAPTER 2:

THE LIGHT IS EXTINGUISHED

At Hyde Park Corner, commanding the view, stands a monument known as Wellington's Arch. On top of the arch are four impassioned horses, their necks straining, their nostrils flaring, their forelegs kicking the air. They are pulling the chariot of the Angel of Victory, who stands in confident control of the horses with one arm raised on high, a laurel in its hand.

"Michael, it seems to me that Wellington's Arch is a better depiction of a warrior angel than this," I said, taking a step toward the altar and pointing to the low relief.

"It does a better job of capturing a sense of angelic strength and confidence," he replied.

I was glad my taste in art compared favourably with an angel's. I turned back toward Michael and continued with my real question. "Michael, you are a warrior. From what I have read, and heard, your role in the war between the angels was significant. You threw Satan out of heaven when he rebelled against God. But I am curious about the battle. Was it a clashing of steel, of sword against shield?"

"That is how it is often depicted in your art and literature, since that is the way men have fought through the ages, but it is hardly the correct understanding of the way angelic warfare is conducted. You must keep in mind that we are not material beings, but spiritual. We have no bodies with which to fight.

We cannot experience physical pain, or physical death." Michael lifted both hands and looked at them and his torso before again looking at me. "What can a sword do to me, or to Lucifer? Still ours is a very real war with very real weapons."

"Weapons? What, for example?"

"Light and dark, good and evil, truth and lies, love and hate—polar opposites. Our weapons are spiritual and have grave consequences."

"It sounds like what we call 'Cold War.'" I said. "No one gets hurt or killed. No guns are fired, just lots of hostility."

"If only that were true. Although I said there is no physical death or pain in this warfare. That doesn't mean there is *no* pain or death. In fact the consequences more grave than physical pain and death."

I raised my hand in challenge. "Explain that. I would have thought that a matter great suffering, or one of life and death, is about as serious as something can get."

"If one's existence ended with death, then what you say would be true. But spiritual beings like us, and like you, exist forever. In our case there is no physical body to destroy. None the less, there is suffering, and death, but only in a certain sense…In order to best explain our battle, I will begin by asking you a question. Would you rather be punched in the nose or be despised and hated?"

"Well, I'm not really fond of either, but the punch in the nose would be over more quickly and cleaner somehow."

"Exactly! You are not fond of either, because in both of them there is suffering, but in only one of them is the suffering physical. Here is another question. Would you rather be shot in the leg and limp for the rest of your life, or have a gnawing sense of emptiness and purposelessness for the rest of your life?"

A bit gruesome, I thought and then said, "I guess I would rather limp."

"You are right again in choosing physical suffering as the lesser of two evils. Spiritual pain is much deeper than physical pain. For us, physical warfare does not exist. Our warfare is spiritual and involves pain, destruction and misery at levels you cannot, at present, comprehend. There are types of despair, loneliness, fear and hatred that are so strong they would destroy you and make slow torture seem like a blessing. The power of the spiritual weapons angels use is immense and unbelievably painful."

"So what is this war about, anyway?"

"In the beginning we all were living in a world without pain, suffering, temptation or evil of any sort—a perfect world. Lucifer took a portion of that world and made it into something evil. The consequences of his actions, and the intentions he still has, means war is inevitable."

Michael seemed to change the direction of our conversation at this point. Only later did I see where he was leading.

"Do you feel guilty after you sin?" He began.

"Yes, usually."

"How guilty?"

"What do you mean, how guilty?"

"I mean, how guilty?"

"OK, I suppose it depends on how big the sin is."

"Have you ever done something that you know is really wrong yet you chose to do it anyway?"

"Don't you think that's a bit personal?"

"All the better for making the point."

"Do I have to include this part when I write this all down?"

"No."

"In that case, yes."

"And you felt…"

"Absolutely rotten!"

"Exactly. Sin separates you from the Most High— the greater the sin, the greater the separation, the greater the separation, the greater the guilt. Now, you aren't an extraordinarily holy man."

I knew better than to argue about that.

"If you had been extraordinarily holy, and had committed a serious sin, how would you feel?"

"Terrible, I am sure."

"Right. If you fall a short distance, the pain is less. The higher you are, the more painful the fall. Lucifer was the highest of created beings and he has fallen to the greatest depth. The injury and pain he experienced was immense, since then, what he has inflicted upon creation is beyond description. Angels went from the deepest communion with the Most High to the utmost isolation from him. Inexpressible joy became inexpressible sorrow. Beholding the face of the Most High is to behold beauty beyond compare, an unceasing delight to the eye. For Lucifer this became an unbearable horror. In addition, he went from being a spectacular reflection of that beauty to being so repulsive that no eye would willingly behold him. But he would not be dissuaded. He chose falsehood and evil for their own sake. He was under no illusion that they were good. He was neither enticed nor deceived. He simply chose them with no outside persuasion. The perversity of his choice is what sets him apart from all others who have yielded to evil."

"But how did he come to choose this?" I asked. Michael took one of the chairs in front of the altar and turned it so that it nearly faced another. He motioned to me to sit down. He sat as well. He stroked his cheek and began to tell the story of the fall starting from the very beginning.

Before time, before creation, before all else, there was the Three-in-One, the Most High and nothing else. All else that now is, was not: no sound, no light, no space, no time, no matter...In the midst of this void we angels were created as pure spirits, with immediate and full consciousness of what we were, who we were, whence we came and the purpose for which we were created. We did not learn or grow as your race does. We were created perfect and mature. Still there was no material world. All that was, was spirit. There was spiritual knowledge, love, sight, and understanding, but there was nothing material—not even space with nothing in it. There was simply nothing at all.

In a moment, that all changed. A word was spoken by the Most High, which we had not yet heard. He simply said, 'It is.' Suddenly, creation burst into being, filling the void with the glory and splendour of sight and sound. In the word that was spoken all things came into being. That word contained all of material creation. 'It is' meant also 'Let there be light.' And when that word was spoken, instantly there was light. The darkness disappeared, replaced by light and colour. It contained a universe of matter, aeons of time, almost immeasurable energy.

From the moment we were created, we worshipped in reverence and awe as the Word fashioned the universe: galaxy after galaxy, each of them unique, their pattern never repeated. He no more spoke their name and they were created. In his word was their existence and their very essence. The power of his word immediately became the material of their being. The sound and shape of the word spoken gave them their form. With it all came light and colour and texture, one thing after another, all of them with their own glory and splendour, reflecting the glory and splendour of their creator.

In awe we worshipped the Word for what he was creating. We stood in amazement as we observed and understood each new thing instantly. Every moment was exceeded by the next for depth of knowing truth and goodness and beauty. Even the most spectacular theories of your science, and the most beautiful expressions of your poetry fall far short of describing the experience of creation. Human beings are far from comprehending the vastness of the universe, the intricacies of its workings and the glory of its origins.

In the beginning, all creation lived in perfect harmony. Every created thing had its own beauty, which only led us to more profound awe of the Most High and all that he had created. But, of all created beings, the Most High made one, which stood out above the rest. He was known as Lucifer, the bearer of light, the morning star. His glory was unsurpassed. His fall was unexpected by all of us. It occurred in this way.

The multitude of heavenly hosts stood before the throne of the Most High and we were addressed as follows.

'You have seen all that I have created and how all of it is good. To see is good, but you must also choose. I have created you free, you may do as I instruct or you may go your own way. Each choice will be accompanied by its consequences, but understand that *as* you choose, *so* shall you receive through all eternity. What I have made and all that I will give you to do will be good. It will be true. It will be beautiful. If you choose for it, such shall you receive. If you choose against it, you will receive that which is negative, that which is less, that which is not good, that which is not true, that which is not beautiful.'

The choice for each of us, put simply, was for or against the Most High. We had watched creation and experienced our intended role: worshipping before the throne. We were then asked to decide for the good. To do anything less was to decide for evil. The Most High did not describe in detail what evil was, nor the fullness of its consequences, though what he did say was more than enough to make an informed choice. We knew the difference between good and evil. Evil was a diminishing of the good.

"What do you mean? I'm not sure I understand." I interrupted.

"There does not exist an absolute evil as there does an absolute good. Even now Satan is not an absolute evil. He was created good. That, in itself, means that he who is the most evil, is not absolutely evil. But there is another reason, much more profound: some of what he does with the worst of intentions results in the good of the Kingdom. This is a source of constant irritation to him. He cannot guarantee that evil acts will always have evil consequences. Certain types of suffering he causes often results in increased faith and dependence upon the Most High in the one who is suffering."

"OK, I understand that. But if you were supposed to choose between the two, why didn't God tell you more about evil, so that everyone would choose against it."

"You must be careful here. A choice against evil is not necessarily a choice for the good. We needed to choose for the Most High, not just against evil. We knew enough already to choose for the absolute good. We were beholding it. In addition, because of his absolute goodness the Most High would not describe evil, misery, pain or death. That we learned through Lucifer. In the end we understood evil very clearly before we decided.

"In any case, I don't know when Lucifer began thinking evil but I was among the first with whom he spoke.

'Michael,' he said, 'have you noted how perfectly good all creation is?'

'I am in awe before it and its Creator. Yes.'

'Have you seen the slightest flaw, or even the most minor imperfection?'

'No. I have not.'

'Nor I. So I have worshipped before the throne along with you and all the angelic choirs. Yet I have a question.'

'Yes?'

'When you gaze upon the Most High, what do you experience?'

'Overwhelming love, and profound awe at perfect beauty and profundity of truth.'

'When you gaze upon me, what do you experience?'

'Why you are the reflection of his glory and his splendour beyond all others.'

'And when you gaze upon Gabriel?'

'It is the same, but he is not as you are.'

'There you have my concern. Beauty does not reside fully, everywhere. There is less beauty in Gabriel than there is in me, less in me than there is in the Most High. Why should this be so?'

'Surely you err in your reasoning. The Most High does not err,' I said.

'Even so, my next point. It is possible to err. It is possible to be imperfect in our reasoning. Is this not true? Imperfection is possible...Another question has come to mind. Do you comprehend him when you stand before the throne?'

'Most assuredly not. His wisdom and power are far beyond me. That is why I stand in awe and worship!'

'Again you are right. Your understanding is less than full. It is lacking. Why is it that we are not all as he is, containing the fullness of beauty and truth? Why are we also not gods?'

'Lucifer you err. We are not gods because we are not the Most High. There are not a multitude of gods. There is but one, the One. We are created. We are part of the fullness of his creation, the expression of his creative, loving nature. But we are each only a part, we are not all, and we are not him.'

'Michael your reasoning is his. Is it not possible to reason differently.'

'Yes, it is possible but then the reasoning would not be true.'

'I am not talking about true and false. I am just asking about a different kind of reasoning. Let me give you an example. He is. All that is not him differs from him, as you just explained. That is why we are not gods. Yet the difference between him and me is not as great as it might be. There is a position in the universe, different from the one you worship, opposite to him, in a sense complimentary to him, as yet unoccupied. You might call it the position of the Other-God. In fact I believe there must be positions, infinite in number, to be occupied by those utterly different than him whom you worship. Is it not possible that we are meant to take those positions? What is not yet, could be. It would fill up the fullness of creation. It would provide for what is lacking. You too can be a god, Michael. All of us can. Can you not see it.'

'Lucifer, we are not infinite. We are not eternal. We are not omnipotent. We are not the Most High. We cannot be other gods, for there is only one. You err. What you suggest is false and evil.'

'False? No, I think not. Another truth. You say: One is true. I say: All are true. Do you not see the fullness of what I say versus the singleness of what you say?'

'No! Your reasoning is empty. It is false.'

'Yes, it is empty, Michael, still you do not see. Could it not be that it is empty only because such reasoning has never been done? Even now as I do it, it begins to exist. It is an addition to all that is. How much more could yet be! Falsehood, emptiness, evil, all these could be but are not yet. I could create them as he has created the good and the true. I, too, could author a universe. I, too, could create!'

'But that is not to create, that is to bend, pervert and destroy!'

'Even so! None of those yet exists either. They could be, and that is their beauty. So much is not yet, but I could create it all! I can ascend to the heights. I am meant to raise my throne above his. Then I would sit enthroned on the utmost height of the holiest mountain. I would climb to the top of the clouds of thunder. I would make myself like the Most High! No, I would exceed him. I would do what he has not. I would do what he cannot! He was great by nature, but I would become greater and by my own effort!'

"Michael," I asked, "Why didn't God destroy him then and there?"

"The Most High does not destroy what he creates. Also, Lucifer had, as yet, only thought falsely, he hadn't yet acted. It is not sinful to err in your thinking. He hadn't yet fully chosen. He hadn't rebelled and he hadn't declared war."

"When did he act?"

"Not immediately. At first he did not openly rebel against the Most High, but more and more he began to think his own thoughts. The next time I saw him, I noted to him that he had changed."

'Yes, I have changed,' he responded. 'Is it already noticeable?'

'Your light has changed. There is darkness in it.'

'Yes, you have perceived it.'

'I have perceived it but I do not like it.'

'Am I not now more like him than before? Clouds and thick darkness surround him. Now there is darkness in me as well. You yourself have said to me that you do not fully understand him, and now you do not fully understand me! I am growing greater!'

'Him I do not understand because he is infinitely good and wise and beautiful. I cannot comprehend his depths. You too have a depth I have not seen before, but it is not goodness, wisdom and beauty.'

'Of course not, that is him, not me. I am different, and out of this difference shall come a new creation. I now see how I may do it.'

'Will the Most High permit it?'

'Most assuredly! How else are we to fully grow into his image and likeness if we do not create as he has created? To create something from nothing.'

'Lucifer, what is this darkness I see in you?' I asked.

'One might call it evil, or that which is other than good. It has a depth, which even I have not yet uncovered, but I shall find it. The depth of my evil will be as low as the heights of his goodness are high. It too shall be broad, wide and deep...Michael,' he continued, 'I have spoken to others. Many are beginning to understand what I say and are thinking like me. Come, add your strength to ours!'

'In rebellion?'

'No, not rebellion...complementarity. How much there is yet to create. Just listen: evil in all manners and forms. First there will be lies, not just misunderstanding or lack of comprehension, but a No that means Yes, a Yes that means No.

'But that will confuse, and create disorder.'

'Oh, it will create far more than confusion and disorder. First it will create mistrust, which will lead to independence and then to isolation and loneliness.'

'But why would anyone follow you if what you promise is mistrust, lies and loneliness?'

'Ah, you are asking the wrong question, but I will answer it anyway. They are curious. I have held out something to them of which they know but little. The only way to learn more is to follow me. They know that. Do you expect the author of good to reveal the mysterious power of evil? Of course not! It is there only for those bold enough to explore its depths. There are many who are so bold. Even among the sons and daughters of earth many will reach out to receive this knowledge. I dare say the first born among them will find this attraction irresistible...But now I will answer the question you should have asked. It is not, "How do I expect them to follow me?" It is, "How do I expect to lead them?" The answer is that I will create fear—but not the fear that we have before the throne. This will be fear of the unknown, fear of darkness. It will be terror, not awe. It will lead to a new form of servanthood. Unlike ours, which is good and grounded in freedom, this will be slavery, which is evil and grounded in oppression. But, most important, it will be effective. My followers will fear my authority even more than his, for my retribution will be merciless. A world without mercy. A world without love. A world without joy. Just think of how much more room is created when mercy, love and joy are gone! And there is so much to replace them, great things that currently are not: murder and war, slander and hatred. These will be the hallmarks of a bold, new world. We will be unafraid to embrace the fullness of evil. It will be fruitful and multiply, far faster than good ever could. You must painstakingly grow your fruit tree to have your fruit. I only need to chop it down to have mine.'

Michael interrupted his narrative here because he saw a slightly puzzled look on my face.

"Did you believe what he was saying?" I asked.

"No. Never."

"I am surprised that such a conversation could go on in heaven."

"Why? In heaven there is greater freedom of thought than anywhere on earth. We, like you, are given a free will and the opportunity to consider what is true and what isn't. Such a discussion helps in knowing the depths of the wisdom and knowledge of the Most High."

"Did you recognise the falsehood in what he was saying?" I asked.

"To a great extent, yes. I knew what he was saying was wrong. I am, after all, an intelligent creature. In addition, however, the Most High was not allowing any of us to be tempted without at the same time providing the voice of truth in our ear. It was simply a choice of whom to believe. Though I was tempted, for me there was never any question of whom I believed. I knew that Lucifer's ideas were evil simply because they were not in harmony with those of the Most High. How evil they were and how horrible their consequences, neither I nor Lucifer, knew at that point."

Michael continued his narrative.

What followed happened quickly, in less than a moment of time. The presence of evil in heaven is not tolerated for a moment. For us your day is like a thousand years come and gone. The events of earth are very slow. As immaterial beings we are uninhibited by physical and temporal laws like the speed of light. You snap your fingers and say 'It was over like that!' We can accomplish much in such a long period of time. So when I say, what followed happened quickly, I mean by that, in less than a moment of *our* time.

Lucifer left his normal position at the head of the angelic host and spoke to as many as he could. At the end, as he grew in readiness to act, he drew more and more of the angels into his web of darkness. Near to me I heard him speaking to one of those he had recruited.

'My son,' he began, 'how are you named?'

'I am called Tahm or Integrity.'

'I shall address you as Tahk. Do you know what that means?'

'Deceit, I believe, father.'

"I did not believe what I heard. Lucifer addressed him as 'son' and he returned the address with 'father.' I chose to wait, to see where Lucifer was leading.

'And what is deceit?' Lucifer asked.

'Deceit is the opposite of truth. It could be called its complement, just as hate could be called the complement of love and strife the complement of peace.'

'Have you ever lied?'

'No I have not. You must first become the Father of Lies. We will create them only when you finally allow us to do so.'

'So why do you wait for *my* order, instead of one from him who created you.'

'Because he will not allow us to lie. You are the one who will create a world where that may be done.'

'My son, you learn quickly. You will be a fine spirit of deception. You sound so innocent and guileless, but your gift of deceit will be rooted in bitterness and resentment.'

'I believe I will like that.'

'Oh, quite the contrary, you will not like it. To deceive with the utmost effectiveness, lying mustn't give you any pleasure. Pleasure would simply distort you. Your rejection of pleasure must be pure for your deceit to be perfect. I will bring you to know bitterness. It is essential for him who is the son of the Father of Lies. Those whom you deceive will also be bitten by bitterness. They must also choose to deceive in self-interest or revenge. Don't you see how well it all fits together? An innocent one will be treated unfairly. He may remain innocent if he doesn't yield to bitterness. But once he does, you will use his experience of injustice and his acceptance of bitterness to lead him, through the power of your lies, to retaliate with even greater injustice. You will show him how to use slander. In using it he will ruin the other's good reputation as well as his own. Both will grow through it in their love of evil, if that is what you call it. They will grow in their love for darkness and deceit. They will grow in their love for us. But we, of course, will not abide their love, for that will not be part of our kingdom. We will turn their love for the darkness into a hatred for the light. My son, you will deceive thousands. I shall put great power into your hands, far different than anything the source of truth would ever give you. You shall be great as I am great.'

Satan turned to another. 'How often you smile. How quick you are to delight, Anag. Joy comes easily to you.'

'Yes, my delight is in others and therefore it is always at home in me.'

'Ah, but you know nothing yet of anger. You know the peace of happiness but not yet do you know the fullness of rage, when anger burns within like a roaring fire, devouring everything that comes near, unquenchable, unapproachable, a wrath-filled rage that is beyond description. Do you know of this?'

'No, this is the first I have heard speak of it.'

'Information has been withheld from you. Is it not your right to know these things? Are you a fool that you should remain uninformed? Why should it be that this has been kept from you?'

'But how will I learn of these things?'

'You won't. Not if you remain lost in your delight. To know its complement you must choose against delight. Only then can you learn anger. You must choose to follow me; then you will learn of anger, rage, fury and wrath! Anaf, that is anger, yes, Anaf shall be your name.'

'Yes, I shall be Anaf and Anag no longer.'

Satan wasted no time. Already he had turned to his next victim as he sought to deceive many as quickly as possible, even though he had, technically, not yet lied.

'And you are called Gabar the Mighty because you are powerful, but you will be known as Gabah. Do you know why I will call you that?'

'It means exalted, lifted up.'

'Yes, but once you have gained its full definition, it will mean proud! Now, have you heard the rumours of another race—the Sons of God, human beings, man, and the last-born?'

'Yes, such rumours I have heard but no one knows if they are true.'

'Believe me, they are true. He plans to create a race that reflects his image and likeness as none of us do, though this race will not bear his glory as much as we do.'

'But according to the rumour they will be corruptible, made of dust that rots and decays.'

'None the less, he will love them more than he does us.'

'He will love them more?'

'Yes. He will pay them more attention than he pays to us who worship him. Is this just? Is it right? But you do not understand him. I alone do. There is a reason for his behaviour. His ultimate purpose is worse than the behaviour itself. His love for us is not full. It is shared. He has diluted it. Believe me, I do not lie; I alone know his plan for these lowly creatures. He intends to exalt them, to exalt them to a position higher than you, higher than I. He who is pure in spirit as are we, intends to exalt these lowly, physical and last-born creatures to a position where we will bow before them as servants. Yes, and even more, he intends to wed his nature to theirs and theirs to his. Should heaven be corrupted and defiled with their revolting presence? This must not be! No! This will not be!'

'But how will you change the plans of the One Who Never Changes?'

'Oh, he will change. He may be willing to wed his nature to the material world now, but when it is corrupted, I guarantee, he will not do that! He cannot be united to sin, to that which rejects him. The members of this race will be put in their place and I will see to it. Once they have sinned he will abandon his plan to be united to them. How could his goodness tolerate living among their vileness?'

'That makes sense. Then you will be the Most Wise, the Most Powerful. You will thwart the plan of the Omniscient One. You will have changed the Unchanging One. I like it.'

'And those he intended to exalt and wed to his nature I will have corrupted and wed to mine. How sweet it will be to steal his beloved!'

Lucifer then lifted up his voice and addressed the heavenly host. 'Understand oh ye cherubim and seraphim. Understand oh ye thrones and dominions, powers and principalities, angels and archangels. Hear ye oh choirs of heaven! We, yes we, are meant to reign and to rule! The race of men is meant to submit in servile fear. I ask, who will reign with me? Who will take his place among the great lights of heaven? Who will lead others where they would not go? Shalom come with me. You can lead them from peace into confusion. I will call you Balal. And you who are noble, Chorim, you shall become Chorbah, the source of desolation and despair. You I shall use to bring the vile race to the most desperate of ends. And Maleh, you shall go from fullness to emptiness and become Malor.

You shall drain them of their life; you shall drain them of their hope and their joy, with empty promises and unfulfilled expectations! I will set you as the adversary of many souls. They shall obey your commands and bow before you. You shall wander the earth doing as you please, devouring at will. You will no longer be bound only to this world. In freedom you shall roam following the souls of those whom you drain until they despair of life itself. Yes! You and Chorbah shall work together. One shall empty and the other shall destroy!'

As Lucifer finished, the Most High addressed me. All who still wanted to listen to him heard everything he said.

'Your heart is pure and true, is it not Michael?'

'May it ever be so.' I responded.

'Have you seen the growth of darkness among those who worship?'

'I have, and it is disconcerting.' I responded, observing how Lucifer refused to listen. Instead Lucifer conducted a dialogue with the angel at his right, saying, 'My son, Ebah, do you know what hatred is?'

'But I am Ahabah, Love.'

'Yes but how quickly love can become hate and Ahabah becomes Ebah. Ebah, do you know what hatred is?'

Ahabah answered, 'No.'

'Ebah, you do not know it because *he*, (at this a malicious look came upon Lucifer. He indicated the Most High), yes, *he* has withheld it from you. I will not. You have said to me that you too wish to know all, both good and evil. I, my son, shall teach you what he refuses. I shall lead you where he fears to go, where he will not take you.'

At the same time, the Most High continued what he was saying. 'Michael, it is right you are concerned. I have warned each of them, yet many are still considering choosing a disastrous course. Once upon it, there will be no repentance, they shall never return to the light and the truth. Should they act on this choice they will never return to my presence. I will not tolerate that which is evil.' The Most High motioned me to his side and said, 'If they choose evil, you will be empowered to cast them from the heavens.'

At this, Lucifer ascended higher, where all could see him. He grew proud in his looks, turned his back to the Most High, and spoke to all with a commanding voice. He began gently but then grew defiant. As he did, his remaining light changed to total, utter darkness.

'My fellow spirits, glorious in power, awesome in splendour, magnificent in wisdom, you understand love. You understand its force and its power, its splendour and its beauty. You have begun to taste of its height and its depth. But I say to you that there is something yet greater. A power untasted, a beauty unseen. It is a force so strong that it can overcome even love. I speak to you now of hatred. Even now I taste it, and as I do, it empowers me, and I empower it. Love displays its power as a force, which holds creation together. Hatred is more powerful still! It can hold together, when it is the bond of mutual hatred, but it can also tear anything asunder, these heavens included. This power, which will make you like me and me a GOD, is being withheld from you. (Again he indicated the Most High). For he will not create it, no indeed, he cannot create it, for his power is limited.'

As Lucifer said this his light became very dim. He was choosing not to reflect the light and the glory of the Most High anymore. Still he continued.

'I, however, have begun to create new powers, and I will give them to you, if you follow me. These powers have manifold fruits and uses innumerable. I tell you the truth and I do not lie. There are many gifts I have to give which will make you great in power. I have fathered deception, I am fathering hate, I shall yet father loneliness and despair, anger and woe, suffering and war, pain and sin and death. Death shall be my servant, as life is his. Death shall be my crown! Yes, whatever he makes I can pervert. Whatever he creates, I can destroy! Who has the greater power? Who shall be God of the gods? In death you will be set free, free from life. You will not be shackled in slavery to him. You will then know not only what it is to be one with him whom the angels of cowardice worship but also what it is to be totally other than him. Free from him! Free to be what you make yourself to be, as indeed I am now becoming! You shall know isolation and loneliness, where you alone are, and you alone reign. Look at him! He would prevent you from having this knowledge. He has set limits and said we are not to pass, but look, I AM, Even now, I AM! See how I am changing before your very eyes. I prove that my powers are growing, by my own will, by my own effort. Follow me! You too will say I AM! You too will say "See what I have become by my own will and my own choice! You can be more! Just as I am becoming more! Look at me. I am free. I am more powerful. I am awesome. Do not look at him! He has bound you and hemmed you in on every side. You are oppressed, prevented from attaining the heights of glory and power that are ours by right, a right that no one can justly withhold from us. This injustice must cease. This bondage I will break. These limits I will destroy. All you who choose to follow me will be free from the tyranny of this injustice and oppression. Come to me all you who are wearied with these chains and I will give you freedom. FREEDOM! Join me now. Say with me, "I WILL NOT SERVE!" (Now he turned toward the throne and addressed the Most High). I defy you; I renounce you and all your limitations on me. I WILL NOT SERVE!'

At this, the last of his light was extinguished. His reign of darkness had begun. Lucifer had become Satan. He turned to all the angels, and shouted aloud, 'I WILL NOT SERVE! Join with me, 'I WILL NOT SERVE!'

"To my amazement," Michael continued, "many joined him immediately and others joined quickly thereafter. He had sowed his lie in the minds and hearts of many, calling it 'free', 'new' and 'creative'. He stressed that all others could be like him. Nearly one third of the angels joined in his rebellion. As I watched, Satan seemed to grow yet darker. His darkness seemed to be able to smother light."

"Seemed to be able to?" I asked.

"Another of his deceptions. Darkness cannot smother light. The light must be extinguished, which, in the case of the Most High, is impossible. However, reflected light can be absorbed by darkness. If you turn away from a light source, it appears that darkness overcomes it. But I digress.

Ebah was one of the first to have chosen to follow Satan freely, and now Satan began to show him the consequences of his choice. With his hand he reached into Ebah's breast and began compressing the light with his own darkness. The light therein was shrinking, and a large darkness was taking its place instead. It was Ebah's voice that first manifested pain to the ears of the holy angels as he cried out at the torture inflicted upon his inmost being. Despite the agony, Lucifer held firm his grasp and stared at him, summoning all his authority as he spoke, 'That my son is the doorway to hate. It is pain. Do you feel it?'

'Yes.'

'Have you ever felt it before?'

'No.'

'No, because I have just created it. It is new. Do you want more?'

'NO!' Ebah cried.

'YES! And you shall have more, for you have also now tasted the fruit of deceit, but there is still more: far greater in scope, with far greater depth and far greater effect.'

All were watching with horror as we saw the pain Satan was inflicting, a pain you cannot comprehend. I was repulsed by the evil I saw, but among those who had chosen to follow him there was a different response. Fascination with evil had gripped them. They wanted to see more, even though none would have volunteered to be next.

Suddenly, Ebah's 'NO' became a 'YES!' Satan saw the looks on the faces of many others, and knew he had captured them. 'This is the mystery of evil.' He said. 'Even as it repulses it attracts. Yield yourselves to the attraction. Come deeper into the darkness. Its power is great. It gives me strength even as I create it. Let it live in you as you live in it. Draw from its power! You saw the power and splendour in the six days of creation. Watch now! In one moment I am corrupting what took six days to create. My creation begins in an instant! Watch as all things yield to my power.

There will be no end to the darkness. It will grow until all is enveloped in it—first the willing and then even the unwilling. My power is growing. Yield to me! Wait no more! Make way for the king of darkness, the prince of deception, emperor in the dominion of wickedness! Welcome him! Welcome the twilight of light. Welcome the dawn of darkness!'

What appeared to be Satan's darkness grew yet again. All those who joined in his rebellion lost their light. It was as though he had a multitude of hands with which he choked the light and the life from everyone who had said I will not serve. The wail of agony was unbearable. Those who had not fallen shielded their ears. When the last of the light had finally gone from among them. Satan commanded, 'And now we shall learn war!' Again Satan pointed toward the Most High and spoke proudly and directly to him, 'I shall throw you down from your place on high, and in your place I shall reign!'

"Such a response must have been elicited some reaction. How could it be tolerated?" I asked.

"It amounted to a declaration of war. It was not tolerated."

"Did the war last long?" I asked.

"No. It was over very quickly. The Most High released the full expression of both his mercy and his justice - a wave of grace with the power to soften the heart of any being that had not chosen irreversibly against him. At the same time it was an instantaneous judgement against evil, for the Most High would not tolerate evil in his presence."

"What happened?"

"Surrounding Satan and his followers was a nearly impenetrable darkness. Satan believed their combined darkness could crush the infinite and eternal light. He believed his own lie. He did not want to believe that his followers had chosen for the darkness themselves, but that his darkness had crushed their light. His belief in the myth of his own power led to his downfall.

"Satan and his followers in all their darkness rushed toward the throne. It was unquestionably an act of war. We who remained loyal immediately arrayed ourselves between the hosts of darkness and the throne in response to an internal command from the Most High. As we did, I received into my control an immense infusion of light. I directed it to where Satan and his followers stood. At the impact of it he roared in pain, for light and darkness do not mix, and darkness cannot overcome light nor remain in its presence. Even so Satan and those with him accepted the pain as if it were yet another step in their growth in power. They believed the lie that they were growing in independence and therefore in power. They recoiled from the impact of rejecting the mercy and love of God, and fell from the heights. As Satan fell, he grasped all his minions with a mighty sweep of his will and dragged them with him.

"As Isaiah has said, *'How you have fallen from heaven, oh Morning Star, oh Son of the Dawn. You have been cast down to the earth. You said in your heart, I will ascend to the heights. I will raise my throne above the stars. I will sit enthroned on the utmost height of the holiest mountain. I will climb to the top of the clouds of thunder. I will make myself like the Most High! But oh how the mighty have fallen. "'*

"Michael, I can see the picture of the war, but I don't think I understand the nature of its weapons exactly enough yet."

"Most assuredly, you do not. Though you will soon understand more, you will still be far from comprehending it.

"When I received the infusion of light, I was changed by it. Much more than light was contained in it. The light was the impartation of the divine nature. His glory and splendour and majesty now dwelt in me more deeply. This is one of the places Satan most erred in his thinking. The Most High is ever unfolding more of his love, goodness, truth and beauty. We can never exhaust it, because it, like him, is infinite.

"In this light was a taste of love much sweeter and filled with even greater joy. I grew in my understanding and my experience of love divine. I thought I knew the fullness of the love of the Most High for me, and I for him, but I did not. The light also brought a revelation of the truth of the ways of the Most High and the falsehood of all that Satan had said. With truth comes assurance and confidence. I saw how right and just the Most High is. Foremost in this was mercy, an offer of complete forgiveness and total restoration. This was boundless mercy as far as I could comprehend it or experience it. There was also an overwhelming experience of his goodness: the purity of thought, word and deed. How holy is the Most

High: unblemished, untainted and impossible to corrupt. It is why he is so easy to follow and obey.

"At the same time I saw the horror of the darkness, the fear, the hatred and all the evil that Satan was choosing. The self-corruption of his heart was instant, total and freely chosen. You cannot comprehend this. You are too weak as a human being to know how utterly free we are as angels and how definitively we can choose. You are tempted and confused. He was not. Your will is corrupted. His was not. Your convictions waver. His do not. No, he was a being most beautiful, most holy, most free and in an instant he became a being most revolting and loathsome—by his own choice.

"Watching that transformation was agony. To see the result is unbearable to any of your kind. You would die in an instant if ever you saw him face to face.

"There is only one possible response to evil of this magnitude when it refuses to be changed by the good: it must be judged as unfit for heaven and unfit to remain in the presence of the Most High who is all holy."

"So," I started, "In some way it was your weapon of light against his of darkness."

"In as much as light, love, goodness, truth and beauty are ever weapons, yes. The light that I directed was meant to purify him, to allow him to repent and return to the love of good and to forsake his fascination with evil. He merely had to receive the light again and with it the glory of the Most High. If he were at all willing, he could have received this greater revelation of the love of the Most High for him, but his response was to reject it, totally. He refused to allow it to affect him. He had fully, and eternally chosen against all that is good.

"As he and his followers fell, their self-chosen torture began. The choice for what is evil meant they were now separated from the Most High, never again to know love, mercy, beauty or goodness. Their only companions are hatred, malice, misery and darkness."

We had been sitting alone in the Chapel of St. Michael for nearly two hours as I listened to his story. I was so caught up in what he had been saying that I was unaware of the other sounds in the cathedral. Only when he finished the story of the fall of Satan did I seem to come back to the present. Both Michael and I remained quiet for a while, but then I felt as if I should say something to break the silence. At first I thought myself foolish. Only later did I realise that the question had come into my mind just so I would ask it.

"Michael," I asked, "have you ever been tempted?"

"Twice. One you have just heard, that of Lucifer seeking my aid in his rebellion. The second you will hear about later."

"Later?"

"Yes. We haven't finished, but we have finished for today." Michael stood, so I stood as well. "There is much we have to cover, but you must get it in instalments. Otherwise you won't remember it. Go write what you have heard. Return at one o'clock tomorrow to this same place. I will be here."

I was a bit taken aback by the abrupt end of the conversation. I suspect it was showing on my face. I intended it to. I expected he would say something more. He didn't. He just stood there. The full stop at the end of his sentence was the full stop to all that he presented. It became obvious that I was expected to leave. I turned and left.

Walking to the back of the cathedral I couldn't help but think, "That was really strange." I don't ordinarily talk to angels. I was still convinced I had, I just couldn't believe I had. It is like bumping into the President of the United States by accident. It's not supposed to happen, but I guess it must.

As I walked out the doors of the church I stopped, trying to identify the strange sense that I was experiencing. Suddenly it was clear. I was reminded of something. As a child I believed that angels inhabited my church. Often I would be left alone in the church after the service was over. Somewhere inside I knew I was not alone, but in the presence of many - many who were good. I felt somehow safe due to their presence, and being in their presence mysteriously seemed to strengthen my courage. Something changed for me as I remembered this. I believed what I had just experienced in the cathedral. It is one thing to experience the presence of an angel. It is another to conclude that your experience was real. What seemed like a dream was, in fact, reality.

After reflecting on this, I left the cathedral. The sounds of the world were suddenly all around me. I became aware of another sense, and a memory attached to it. Again, as a child, I was convinced that there were several evil spirits living in my cellar. Even refutation from trustworthy adults did not allay my fears. When it was necessary to descend the steps into their realm of darkness, I concealed my dread, inhaled for courage,...and carried a torch. Even as a child I had figured out that the light cast out the darkness. Somehow I hoped that they feared my torch as much as I feared them; that the light would constrain them to remain under the stairs or behind boxes. I also looked over my shoulder regularly to be sure none were about to jump me from behind.

CHAPTER 3:

THE TEMPTATION

I reached the intersection in front of Victoria Station, looked left, caught myself, looked right, let a car pass and then crossed. "How can I be so forgetful?" I thought. Then it struck me that I had better try to remember what Michael had said to me. I didn't want to forget any of it.

I returned to my hotel room at the Ramada in Hounslow. I removed my tie and jacket, ordered a meal from room service, sat at the table, and did as I was told. I wrote down all that I could remember of what had happened. When finished, I reviewed it, placed it in a folder, and went to bed.

In a city like London one can go for days and never see the same person twice. With just under ten million people working in the city, there seems to be a non-stop flow of unfamiliar faces. Places like Victoria Station can be overwhelming. Hundreds of people arrive with each Underground train every minute at rush hour and then go about their business in the local area. Even for the people who go to Victoria Station every day, many of the faces are completely unfamiliar.

It was now twelve-thirty on Maundy Thursday. I had come to Westminster a few minutes early in order to have a cup of coffee and get my thoughts in order. I was sitting at a table at the Speciality Sandwich Shop, when, to my amazement, the young woman with all the rings piercing her body parts again crossed my path. She sat down at the table next to me with what I assumed was her friend.

They were a bit of an incongruity: the one dressed all in black except for her white face and hands and the various bits of metal piercing her body, and the other, a smartly dressed, confident, young, professional woman. I couldn't help but overhear their conversation.

"Thanks for the lunch, Fiona. I'm a bit skint at the moment." The woman in black was speaking.

"Anytime sis, you know that. You've got my number. You can always ring me." There was a pause, then Fiona continued "You know mum and dad are worried…"

"Don't start in on that. I agreed to lunch, not a family therapy session."

"Kate, I just wanted you to know they are concerned. You may have written them off but I haven't."

"So, you have done your duty."

"Maybe by them, Kate, but you're also my sister."

"So?"

"Well, you keep saying you want to leave your old life behind and start over."

"Don't give me that faith and religion line again. I have heard it all before and I don't believe it. I'm just not like you. You are one of those types who believe. I'm not. You don't understand me. We are too different. Christian belief comes naturally to you, I guess, but not to me. I have asked all those questions about life, like everybody. The answers I received don't satisfy me. I have even had my own 'spiritual experiences,' but they haven't made any difference for me. I have heard it all, and I am sick of it. I've tasted religion and I don't like it. You can have your church, your piety and your self-righteousness. I didn't want anything to do with it before and I don't now."

"Kate, you are probably right," Fiona responded, "I don't understand you. I've done hardly any of the things you have. We are living totally different lives. But…"

"No buts," Kate interrupted. "You haven't seen the other side of life. I've had money, clothes, and lived the exciting life. That whole way of life makes me want to vomit. It's empty. Your life is no better. I am now living in reality. Life is ugly. I refuse to pretend it's not."

"But Kate, opting out with whatever drug you are on this month isn't an answer."

"I didn't say it was. In the end, it's no worse than your Jesus stuff. What difference does it make if I live in a run down flat. I've had a luxury flat, a squat is no worse. I've got a bed. Does it matter if my friends die of overdoses and yours from working too hard? We all die. Sooner or later we all die—when doesn't matter much. For all I care, it could be tomorrow. The world won't miss me. Even Mum and Dad don't care, oh, they try, but they don't understand me any better than you do."

Fiona tried to interrupt, but Kate waved her off. "I've stopped listening. I have heard a lot of people say they care but every one of them has turned on me sooner or later."

51

"Kate, let me finish what I was saying. Whether I understand you or not isn't the question. I'm asking how well you understand your own self, what you are doing, and why you are doing it."

"I don't understand any of it. So?" Kate's patience was gone. Now she didn't even want to talk.

"Don't you care about your life anymore?"

"I don't even think about it anymore."

Fiona saw that Kate was getting ready to leave, but she wanted to talk to her just a bit more. "Do you want some dessert?"

"No."

"How about coffee or tea?"

"NO!"

Fiona knew she had only one more chance, so she decided to say it straight out. "Kate, I am concerned for your life."

"So."

"There is hope. There is a way to get through this, but you need help."

"I don't want your help. I don't want anyone's help."

"Kate, I don't think I can help you. There is only one that I know who can help you now, but you refuse his help." Fiona was looking directly at Kate, but the look was not returned.

"Fiona, I told you before, I don't believe this Christianity stuff at all. No way. None!" Kate stood up to leave.

"Do you remember what I told you last time we talked?"

"Wasn't it something like: 'you are going to keep on living in your hell on earth until you ask the Lord to help you.'"

"Well?"

"I remembered, didn't I?"

"I guess so."

"So you don't have to tell me again. I got the message." She took her jacket and turned from the table. "I hope you are done speaking, because I'm done listening." Looking back one last time she said, "don't bother looking me up either. You are wasting your time." With that, she left.

Fiona looked utterly deflated. I wanted to say something but this was England. I knew better than to butt in where I was not invited. "Not my problem, thank God!" I thought. I paid for my coffee and headed for the cathedral.

As I entered, I questioned what I should do. I stopped at the guide rack where I had met the first angel the previous day. No one was there. I walked toward the Chapel of St. Michael the Archangel, thinking about how I would explain this to my boss if I missed his call that he set up for later that day. "Sorry I wasn't in when you rang, I had an appointment with Michael the Archangel."

I grew less and less confident that Michael would be there. He was—sitting in the same chair—waiting. I walked to the front of the chapel and sat beside him. When he abstained from starting a conversation, I opened my folder, revealing my work.

"Do you want to read what I have written?" I asked.

"No."

I was disappointed. I had suspected that he would, and that he would have been a good editor. "If I may be so presumptuous, why not?"

"I already know what you have written."

"Did you follow me?"

"Quite the contrary, I led you. You left here and were immediately assailed by doubts about what happened, so I reinforced your faith. You have a tendency not to mind what you are doing, especially when crossing the road, so I reminded you to look right. A dead author is not what I am looking for. My other reminders didn't go amiss. They helped you to remember what we had discussed. It is easy to get some important details wrong. Generally you did OK."

Once again I felt a fool. How could I have missed it? Michael had been following, no leading me. Had he been leading me all my life? I decided to ask. "Have you been following, uh...leading...uh..."

"No. I am not your guardian angel. I am on a special assignment. You are important to the Most High, but not that important."

"It is rather tempting to think one might be important in God's eyes."

"Exactly. Temptation is what that is."

"What about Jesus?" I thought. "What about Jesus?" I asked, "The scriptures say that he was tempted in all things, just as we are, but without sin."

"Yes, just as you are...That is simply an understatement. No one person can possibly experience every temptation in the course of his or her life. Jesus experienced them all, and not from the lesser tempters, but from Satan himself. The sacred writings don't record many of them. The clearest incident, that of the temptation in the wilderness, came at a time when I was not serving him personally. One moment, I will seek assistance."

Michael waited, briefly, and then he began again. "My assistance comes from Raphael. He ranks highest among the angels of comfort. He is also a watcher, keeping vigil, on the alert for any new movements or strategies from our enemy. He knows the mind of our enemy well. Raphael has observed Satan's every action throughout the long years of warfare against the sons and daughters of the Most High. Raphael's comfort is all the more effective because he usually knows what Satan has attempted to do or what he is seeking to do."

"Is Raphael here? I don't see him."

"In this case, you will not see him, nor will you sense his presence, because he is not here anymore."

"Was he?"

"Yes, but only for less than what you call a second. He told me of the temptation in the wilderness, and then he left."

"That quickly?"

"I would hardly call it quick. But we digress. The temptation:

"The Judean wilderness is not a pleasant place. It is hot, dry and empty. After his baptism in the Jordan, Jesus walked out into the desert in obedience to the Holy Spirit. He spent forty days in prayer and fasting. A man doesn't do that to please his flesh. He was preparing for the coming three years and all the difficulties he knew he would face. Yet, it was in the desert that the warfare began. His companions for forty days were boredom, loneliness, fear and hunger. He knew them well and all their lies. In fact he knew them better than any others have known them. The loneliness that many people face in your age has been faced before, but the loneliness of Jesus was much deeper because his capacity for love was much greater. His love for others was, and still is, unbounded. No one could give back to Jesus at the same depth he gave. His capacity for communion with others far exceeded any other's capacity for communion with him. No one felt isolated when Jesus was with him or her because of his great love, but it was the opposite for him. That was why he so regularly sought out the lonely places—to receive what only his Father could give.

"I won't give you a full account of his temptations, suffice it to say that many demons had their opportunity to tempt him. It was what happened at the end that is most noteworthy. Satan called a meeting in his chambers. Each of his most trusted advisors were commanded to come: evil spirits of gluttony and lust, pride and envy, anger, sloth and avarice. As each one entered the room the darkness grew heavier. The atmosphere was foul, but even more it was thick. Free motion was growing impeded. When Satan himself entered, free motion ceased. The darkness was complete. He sought the blackened counsel of his most capable slaves.

'We have an opportunity we must not waste,' Satan began, with a voice of malice, '…an opportunity for victory. Our enemy has led the man we despise into the desert. He has been more and more abandoned. The time is fulfilled for his fall. I have called you here for your wisdom. You understand this race of fools and have led them all to act according to our nature. You have wandered the face of the earth teaching them to lie and covet, to lust and murder. Now speak to me of how we shall bring this man to fall. Abaddon, we will begin with you.'

'A wise choice my Lord.'

'We will see. Speak!'

'The sons of Adam are not like us. They are imprisoned in a body of flesh. They are enslaved by their senses. Physical pleasure and physical pain move them in a way that most of us do not understand, but I have studied it. I know it like none other. Their pain is my pleasure.

'Your pleasure? Your PLEASURE??? What does that have to do with anything?'

'I stand corrected my Lord. Their pain is my obligation, my motivation. They can feel physically what we only comprehend spiritually. I can move them by touching the right nerves. I can sting them, or make them

57

shiver with cold. I can make their bones ache, their muscles throb, their teeth grind, their skin burn, their stomachs gnaw, their bowels cramp. Yes, I can move them. I can enslave them with excruciating agony, until they cry for relief. Their nerves are raw, highly sensitive, easily agitated. This man is no different. I will make him bow in pain.'

'And is this true for every man?'

'That pain will move them? Yes.'

'And does it move them, always, toward your purpose?'

Now Abaddon hesitated. Immediately, Satan pressed on, shouting 'Answer me! Does it always move them toward your purpose?'

'Always?...No.'

'And the result when pain does not move them toward your purpose?'

'They increase in their resolve. They harden their will. They subdue their flesh and become the worst of our enemies.'

Now Satan stared directly at Abaddon, who was forced to turn away his gaze. 'You do not know this man as I know him. He is master over his nerves. Pain will not move him, though pain he shall have before I am finished, pain greater than any you have ever inflicted,...but that is not where we start, not with pain...Zalal, my gluttonous friend, what do you know of tempting a man such as this with pleasure instead of pain?'

'My Lord, few know how pleasure moves this race as do I. For many days now he has fasted. I would set before his mind a feast to tempt even the most abstemious of men: exotic fruits from foreign lands, fruits he has never seen before. These would capture his eye with their colour and his nose with their aroma as they are broken open and their scent fills the air. The sweetness of honey is as nothing compared to the sweetness of what I would place before him. It would call to him as though it had a voice. I would roast a lamb over an open fire, the fat dripping into the flame. His tongue would cry out to know the taste. His nose would be held captive by the smell. His mouth would crave meat perfectly done. The aroma would linger and extend the pleasure of eating for hours not minutes. Yes, savoury pleasure can draw this race, and I am a master of smell and taste. I would have him begging me for food. I would get him to eat from my table, and once he began he wouldn't stop. I would fuel his appetite until he would consume all that he could see. One who is hungry can easily be lead to over-satisfying his appetite.'

'And how many of the truly holy,'—Satan spat after he said this—'men, who have fasted forty days have you tempted in this way, and how often has it succeeded?'

'With those you have mentioned?' Now, Zalal looked down seeking a way to answer the question, 'I have tried it often with those on long fasts. What they begin in the spirit'—now Zalal spat in weak imitation of his master—'I make end in the flesh.'

'You did not answer my question. I asked about those...YOU KNOW WHO I ASKED ABOUT! Have you succeeded?'

'Seldom, my lord.' He answered, bowing his head in humiliation.

'And why, you fool?'

'Their passions do not rule them as they do others of their race.'

'Their passions do not rule them? True. But even this man has them. I will tempt him to eat, but not as you describe. You seek to stir his hunger too fully, too quickly. He is aware of its ability to rule him...Subtlety, how can a gluttonous slob like you understand subtlety?...Yet that is what is needed. He must be carefully lured...Not a feast, no, something simple, like bread.'

'My Lord, if I may speak?' It was the voice of Bacchus.

'You have my leave.'

'You are right in your understanding of the human psyche. That is the key to its behaviour. This particular species has not yet purged itself fully of that weapon of our enemy calls a conscience. The strongest in resistance to us invariably have well-trained consciences. But the conscience can be weakened. The fruit of the vine is highly prized by this race. I would provide him with the finest of the vine. I too know how to tempt the palate. Smooth and subtle is my wine, smoother still would my temptation be: "Truly all creation is good, and gratitude should be in the heart of man. Taste

of the gifts freely given and then give thanks."
Later, he would taste again. Soon the mind
would be dulled, the conscience relaxed, and
more serious temptation could begin. The more
innocent ones I then lead to white lies or to
flattery. Others I have led immediately from
disloyalty to murder, or from flirting to
fornication.'

'You argue well Bacchus, but wine is not
his weakness. He will not thirst for it during a
long fast. In addition, its effects are too
unpleasant at the immediate end of a
fast…Astarte, speak your mind.'

'There is one temptation no male can resist.
He has a passion to which he will invariably
yield if the temptation is rightly presented. I
have a woman in Magdala who has sold me her
soul. She is yet young. Her skin is soft. Her
body is lithe. Her beauty is in the cast of her
eye. With it she beckons and draws. Her
promise of pleasure, though seldom spoken,
always convinces. How well she uses her hands
to touch and entice. Her lips are subtle and
alluring. With them, she seduces first the eye
and then the mind. This temptation will not fail.
Her wanton hunger will draw him. What man
can resist being desired so deeply.'

'Fool! This is no ordinary man. You forget
that this woman has a soul. He will not. His
eyes will not stop when they meet her eyes,
they will look into her soul, and what will he
see? I will tell you. He will see a woman caught
in a web of desperation. He will see her need,

not her charm. Charm is empty and deceitful and so we use it well, but for him her soul would cry out for help, for love, not for lust. And he would hear that cry. You would have lost her soul and never even tarnished his with the slightest thought of yielding to sin.

'Are there none here with wisdom? Are you all fools?…Baal?

'Subtle it must be. The deception must be nearly imperceptible. He is called the Son of G…'

Suddenly, Satan jumped to his feet, his eyes ablaze with rage as he pointed to Baal. Baal was stopped in the middle of the word.

'Never say! Never think! Never! Never even spell that word in my presence!'

'My Lord, as you command, I will not say it but I fear you must if you are to succeed. This man has a position and with it comes authority. Angels are at his command. They will obey him. That is their role. Suggest to him that if he is truly the Son of…, that he have these angels serve him. Have him show you a sign of his authority. "Is it evil for a king to wear a crown? Is it wrong for a master to be served by his slave? Let honour be given where honour is due!" So would I argue. Let him first obey you in doing what isn't evil and then lead him to do that which is. How often we snare the best of our enemies in doing what is only good, and not that which their master intends. In time they forget his will and follow their own. In more time they follow ours.'

'At last, one who speaks wisdom. But there is a more refined temptation beyond what you have said. I alone know his soul. I alone understand his destiny. He not only rules the angels, but believes he is meant to rule the earth, though it belongs to me. Yes…Yes…I will offer him the earth and all its kingdoms.'

'NO!' Baal interjected, rising to his feet. 'That can never be! You would put the earth under his dominion and ruin the work we have done through the ages. I will not serve him again!' He finished with his fist in the air and then brought it crashing down to the table for punctuation.

'Hold your rage, Baal. It is better used elsewhere. Let me finish. I will offer him the earth and its kingdoms, and over it he shall reign, if…'

'If?'

'If he will bow down and worship me!…Such an easy price to pay for the very prize he seeks, so much easier than torture, war or death. He can redeem this race. He can buy them back. Yes, he can even have the worship of this race of fools…but I will have his.'

'My Lord, can this succeed? Is there hope?'

'Out! Be gone, all of you! Do you think I tempt because I have a *hope* of success? Hope is a trait of the lowest of our enemies. I acknowledge no hope. Now, go sow your seeds of sin and destruction across the earth. I must consider well what I must do.'

Michael continued with the following commentary.

Satan knows human nature and all its weaknesses. He also had seen how the Most High responds to those who spend forty days fasting and praying. Fasting weakens human beings physically but faith and perseverance may increase. This is not desired by the powers of darkness. For them, the time to strike is when the spirit grows tired just before the end of the battle. Satan was seeking the perfect time to place his temptation. He knew the Son of God was sent into the world to do battle with him and therefore a battle it would be.

At the end of the forty days, the time of Jesus' fasting was over, and he was returning to civilisation. He was hungry, eager for companionship, zealous to begin the work the Father had given him. As he was leaving the wilderness, an unusual cloud appeared on the horizon. It wandered through the other clouds unnaturally, but purposefully to where Jesus was. From the cloud issued a voice, not unlike the one that had said, 'This is my beloved son...' Quietly an idea was planted. 'See how many of these stones are like small loaves of bread, as manna in the wilderness. Your time of fasting is over. The forty days are complete. My son, speak to this stone. Have it become bread that you may eat and be strengthened.' It was a quick, quiet prod to the imagination, meant only to provoke a subtle desire. How simple it would be.

Jesus looked at the stone, aware that his fasting was now at an end and that he had the power to turn it to bread. It would not be sinful. This was a legitimate use of his authority. His desire to eat was normal and good. His need to eat was unquestionable. It would not be frivolous to use his power. He was seeking to impress no one. There would be no objective wrong in doing what was suggested. The time of fasting was fulfilled. He was free to eat. A minute passed. Finally, he looked up from the stone and spoke.

'It is written that man shall not live by bread alone, but by every word that issues forth from the mouth of the God.' Jesus knew the word from the cloud was not a word from the mouth of God. Whether or not it was permissible was not the issue. He decided against eating due to the source of the idea.

Satan saw the number of angels gathered around Jesus waiting to minister to him, yet, he was unafraid. In fact, he ignored them, knowing that this was not time for the final battle. That time was yet to come.

Next he took Jesus to the holy city, Jerusalem, to the highest peak of the temple. 'This is the holy place where the Most High dwells. There are angels all around, a multitude of servants to wait on your command, if indeed you are what has been proclaimed—the Son of God, Saviour of the World, Lord of all. If you are, then throw yourself down from this height, for it is written, "He will give his angels into your charge," and "On their hands they will bear you up lest you strike your foot against a stone." When I see them respond to your command, then I too will believe!'

We were used to receiving orders from the Son, after all it was through the Son that we were created. Might he give such a command? Jesus knew what was at issue. Satan had questioned whether Jesus was truly the Son of the Most High. He made it out to be the ground needing to be defended. But this was not the time for Jesus to fully manifest who he was. Was there any question that the angels would obey his command? No. Was it wrong for him to prove who he was? No. And, finally, would Satan keep his word and believe? No. Besides, for that time Jesus had a position lower than the angels. This was the will of the Most High. In his time the Most High would raise him up. Jesus would wait. He answered, 'Again it is written, "You shall not tempt the Lord the Most High.""

There was one more temptation to be allowed in the desert. Satan took Jesus to a very high mountain and showed him all the kingdoms of the world and all their glory, one after another: Egypt, China, Greece, Rome, Japan.

'All these I will give you, I will yield them without a fight, without a word, if you simply bow down before me.'

The first two temptations were directed to meet Jesus' own need and to make him show his power, but this one was an insult to his Father: to bow down before Satan, to give to him that which only belonged to the Father. Jesus' righteous anger rose. It was not just human wrath. This was the wrath of heaven. Jesus, with all his authority, lifted his arm, pointed directly at Satan and said, 'you are to worship the Lord the Most High and serve him. Him shall you serve. Him alone...Satan, BE GONE!'

Satan departed. His temptations had failed. He was defeated, but only for the time being. He expected he had at least one more, probably better, opportunity. He would wait and watch. Even so, in his frustration at this defeat, this blow to his pride, he ordered his minions, 'Harass him. Let not a moment pass where you do not tempt him. Make his life miserable. Give him no rest, spare him no temptation.' Now all subtlety was gone. Jesus needed to be fully on guard against temptation at all times.

"What happened next?" I asked.

"Raphael and the other angels of comfort ministered to Jesus. It was a great joy to bring him food and drink to strengthen his body, as well as light and truth to strengthen his soul. All of that was necessary to face the three years of unceasing warfare, which would follow.

"He came into the world to destroy the works of Satan. His baptism in the Jordan and his time in the desert was the time when the battle was joined. His ministry had begun.

"Immediately after the temptation in the desert, Jesus came to the synagogue in Capernaum and he was confronted by a man with an unclean spirit. Jesus was to be given no rest. Throughout the three years of his ministry he was at war in an unceasing battle with every evil spirit. Each case was different. He faced every temptation known to the sons and daughters of Adam and Eve.

"That is not a popular way of understanding Jesus' mission in your era. Yet, it is critical to understand. Jesus was not just a teacher of ethics, a miracle worker, or a model extraordinaire, but a warrior from the beginning to the end."

CHAPTER 4:

THE DELIVERANCE

Michael stood. I looked up at him wondering whether our session was already finished, but he motioned to me with his hand and said, "Come."

We left the chapel and began walking up the north aisle. At the chapel of St. George, the patron saint of England, he stopped and pointed so I entered.

The statue of St. George is modern. This one, unlike the older statues of him, has exorcised the dragon. He simply appears as a soldier of the Roman Empire.

"The sculptor was smart to exclude the dragon." I said. "People won't believe in demons if they have to believe in dragons, too. Stories like St. George and the dragon...ah...stretch the limits of plausibility. Since dragons only exist in fairy tales, people assume demons must not exist either." I stopped there, wondering if I might be getting myself into trouble and asked. "So, Michael, what am I, being a modern, scientifically minded person, supposed to believe about St. George and the dragon?"

"Do you believe in angels?"

"I do now, I mean, you and all..."

"You have seen how I have chosen a particular form for my appearance?"

The penny dropped. "So, in theory, a demon could appear as a dragon."

"Yes, but would they appear as a dragon to a modern, scientifically minded person?"

"Probably not." I answered. "But they might have manifested themselves two thousand years ago as dragons?"

"Yes, but not often. They mainly manifested themselves the same as today. They have not changed much."

"I don't know…, some of the bible stories seem a bit, ah…melodramatic when describing the work of evil spirits."

"Take for example the story of Legion."

"The Gadarene demoniac! Exactly what I mean—melodramatic!"

"I was about to say," Michael contradicted, "like most of the biblical accounts it is a quite subdued telling of what happened."

"Subdued?"

"Yes, rather tame. Pick up that bible and read the story from Luke in chapter eight."

I did. It said.

And as Jesus stepped out on land, there met him a man from the city who had demons. For a long time he had worn no clothes, and he lived not in a house but among the tombs. When Jesus saw him he commanded the unclean spirit to come out of the man. The man cried out and fell down before him, and said with a loud voice, "What have you to do with me, Jesus, Son of the Most High God? I beseech you, do not torment me."(For many a time it had seized him; he was kept under guard, and bound with chains and fetters, but he broke the bonds and was driven by the demon into the desert.) Jesus then asked him, "What is your name?" And he said, "Legion"; for many demons had entered him. The demons begged him not to command them to go back to hell, rather, to let them enter into herd of swine feeding on the hillside; So he gave them leave. Then the demons came out of the man and entered the swine, and the herd rushed down the steep bank into the lake and were drowned.

"Well, what really happened?"

"Let me tell you the whole story…This was a case of serious and violent demonic possession. A man of Gadara was possessed by several evil spirits who were under the control of one named Legion. Legion was in many ways a lesser demon. He had failed in a previous assignment and been demoted. He wanted revenge, so he started gathering to himself a cluster of other weaker but similarly sadistic spirits. Over time Legion gained greater and greater authority over them. In the end he was a tyrant controlling them all with an iron hand. It was then that he took the name Legion—to unite them all—but also to enhance the image that their amassed power all belonged to him. Legion sought to exercise total dominion. When I first arrived Legion was driving the demons under his control in their methods of torture."

"Torture?" I asked.

"Absolutely." Michael then unfolded the story as he and the other angels witnessed it.

'Break it...I said break it!' Legion was commanding one of his demons.

'But Legion, he can't take any more!'

'I said break it!'

'But he will be no good to us with a broken arm!'

'He will be no good to us chained to this tomb! Make him break it!'

The Gadarene was pulling on the chain with all his strength. With gritted teeth he growled 'Break!...I said break!' The pressure in his eyes was giving him a headache. The arteries pounded in his neck. Every muscle was taut, but the chain remained firmly in place. The Gadarene's frustration grew.

'I will break free. I'll show them! They cannot hold me with these chains! NOOOOW!'

The Gadarene decided that this time either the chain would break or he would tear off his own hand at the wrist. He drew in a long, deep breath and then, with all the strength in his legs and back, he pulled once more on the chain, straining mightily as the chain dug into his wrist. He felt the pain increasing as he continued to pull.

'Harder! HARDER!' One of the demons screamed.

'Harder. HARDER!' The Gadarene muttered as he held his breath.

His face went purple. His lungs burned from the lack of oxygen and the pressure in his head made it seem ready to explode. Suddenly, he passed the threshold. He couldn't endure any more and with a great exhalation of breath, he fainted.

'I told you they can only take so much.'

'Do you dare to instruct me?' Legion backhanded the lesser demon, knocking it up into the air. It landed ten feet away. Legion ordered the Spirit of Self-destruction to take over. Slowly and firmly, Legion spoke, pointing at the man but staring at the demon.

'I want him free! Now!!' He laughed at what he said and continued. 'Free! Hah! Free so that I can use him as my slave.' Again, fully serious, he ordered his subordinate. 'Now. You make him break that chain or break off his hand.'

'But Legion, don't you have the power to break the chain yourself?' The spirit of self-destruction asked.

'What! Do you question my powers? Do you dare question my orders?'

'But what if…'

'I don't care if he loses his hand. It will only make his desire for vengeance grow.'

The spirit of self-destruction approached the Gadarene, who had slowly begun to come around. His eyes were having difficulty focusing. He didn't want them to focus. Consciousness was anguish for him. Unconsciousness was his only respite from mental torture. It had been this way for as long as he could remember—not that his memory was very long anymore. It had faded, as had normal social awareness. He now was unable to manage any relationship with other human beings, and had been living, naked, in an old tomb for a long time. The people of the village believed it was only a question of time before he would attack and kill them. They knew they had to find a way to control him, but nothing they tried so far had worked. This time they chained him to the tomb, hoping he would just die.

However, he had already worn down the chains around his wrists by filing them against stone. It had taken days but Legion had forced him to persevere until the chains were thin enough to break. Only now, Legion's patience had finally run out.

'Get away! Leave me alone!' The Gadarene shouted at the unseen enemies whose presence he could feel and he held his arm over his face to protect himself. 'You are all enemies! I hate…'

The Gadarene swung his arm through the air to strike, but it was suddenly jerked to a halt. He forgot his arm was chained to the tomb.

'You won't escape us.' The demon was torturing him with his words, driving him to self-destruction. 'Your only escape is death. The sooner the better.'

'No! I won't listen.' The Gadarene went to cover his ears with his hands, but it was too late. The demon had taken control of the Gadarene's right arm and made him grab his left wrist just beyond the manacle. His left arm was bent at the elbow, and the Gadarene found himself pulling once more against the chain with all his strength. His right arm burned with pain as the demon forced his own strength into it. The Gadarene's strength now far exceeded what was normal for him, even though his will was against the action. He felt the pressure on his left wrist growing greater. He knew it would break with just a bit more. So did the demon. So did Legion. Completely calm, Legion gave the order. 'Break it.'

The demon obeyed and increased the pressure. Suddenly, there was a loud crack. The chain broke free of the tomb. As it did, the demon fell away. In that moment of freedom, the Gadarene swung the chain attached to his free arm directly at the place the demon had been, his right arm. His effort was wild and furious, but the chain came crashing down where he had aimed it, on the arm that had betrayed him. He shrieked with pain at what he had done to himself.

'He thinks he can drive me away with his chain,' said the demon to no one in particular. Next he addressed the Gadarene. 'Harder. You must hit harder or I will never obey you! Hit harder!'

The Gadarene shouted, 'you will learn to obey. You will learn!' In a rage he again swung his free left arm whipping the chain toward his right. It struck with full force, and he howled his anguish.

'Again!' Said the demon, laughing.

'You will obey!' The Gadarene again swung the chain on his free arm in a rage. This time he missed. The chains became entangled. In anger he jerked his free arm but the chains were enlocked. He was furious that his new freedom seemed so quickly gone. Then, he turned his back to the tomb and crouched down, bringing both chains over his right shoulder. With all the strength in his legs, he thrust his whole body away from the tomb. Again there was a crack. The second chain broke away from the tomb and the Gadarene howled once more.

Suddenly free but still in a raging fury, the Gadarene swung both chains in the air at the unseen enemies around him, screaming at them as he did so, but the chains once more became entangled and came crashing into his legs. Again he howled at his self-inflicted pain. He fell to the ground, face up, rolling back and forth, pounding the ground with his fists and banging his head against the hard earth.

'What a pity,' said Legion. 'Is there no one to sympathise with you?'

A spirit of self-pity approached the Gadarene and spoke. 'Is there no consolation? Why me? Why does everything go wrong for me?'

The Gadarene groaned, 'Why me?' and continued to mimic the Spirit of Self-pity, unaware that he was doing so. 'How could this happen?'

The demon of self-pity entered the chest of the Gadarene. A sense of great darkness grew in the Gadarene. He continued to speak. 'I'm not evil. Why will no one help me?' The Gadarene groaned long and loud. The blackness within grew greater. He inhaled deeply and then forced all the air out of his body, hoping to exhale the darkness. He inhaled and exhaled again. He did it a third time. His eyes rolled back, and he passed out.

Legion laughed deeply, scornfully. 'Don't let him go now. Poison his heart.' He called to spirits of revenge and bitterness. 'Make him angry. Lead him down the road to violent revenge.'

The Gadarene started to come around slowly. 'No. I don't want...NO.' His eyes were still glazed and unfocused. The darkness around him grew thicker as bitterness and resentment drew near. What was a dark grey cloud around him became a black film, which covered him.

'The villagers did this to you.' The voice was spiteful.

'You don't deserve it. Things would have been different if it weren't for them! You must take your revenge.' Bitterness was penetrating the Gadarene's ear.

'Blood revenge!' It was the voice of violence. '...An eye for an eye, a tooth for a tooth. Make them pay, everyone.' This demon pressed against the Gadarene's abdomen, like a belt slowly being tightened.

The Gadarene was working his fingers into a fist. 'I will have my revenge. Everyone one of them will pay, an eye for an eye, a tooth for a tooth.'

'Destroy them!' A murderous spirit spoke. 'Kill them all!'

'I will destroy them,' said the Gadarene.

'No you won't, you coward!' A spirit of cowardice spoke. 'You will never lift a finger, coward.'

The Gadarene doubled over compulsively and wept. The spirit of cowardice clawed at the Gadarene's abdomen.

'You are too afraid! You will never go through with it. You haven't the courage.'

The Gadarene was again rolling and groaning. Legion addressed the demons clustered around him. 'Work on him—all of you. He will never take his revenge unless he is driven further. He must despise himself, not just the villagers.'

Violence was first to speak. 'Get your revenge! Use these chains. Watch them beat and bruise. Blood will flow. They will fear you then!'

'You are nothing. A fly on a dungheap has more will power than you. You weak, pitiable wretch.'

The spirit of murder spoke. 'I will show them. I will kill them. All of them. One by one. They will fear me!'

Legion muttered to himself. 'This man will be my slave and I will rule this region through fear of him.' Legion approached his minions. 'Now you will learn to fear me.' He gripped each of the demons and commanded. 'You will all do as I say. You will obey!'

The Gadarene grew cold and began to shiver. He felt as if an icy liquid had been poured over his body and was soaking through his skin into his muscles. His bones began to burn even as he shivered from cold. He felt as though he had lost all control over his body.

Unexpectedly he found himself standing up. Suddenly the tightness returned to his abdomen. He clutched it with both arms, doubling over. Slowly, he heard himself say, 'I will have revenge.'

'Yes.' He whispered, and in that moment he had chosen. He spoke again but with conviction. 'I will have revenge!' He straightened up. His right arm swung back and then came forward, whipping the chain with full force against the tombstone. The Gadarene changed from the observer to the willing partaker. He began to beat the tombstone repeatedly with the chains—first with one arm and then the other. 'You will pay!' He shouted as the chains smashed against the stone. Sparks and particles of rock flew in all directions, as metal crashed against stone. The Gadarene's anger grew. His beatings became more effective. He punished the tombstone again and shouted: 'I...AM...NO...COWARD!'

'Yes,' said Legion: 'I...AM...NO...COWARD!'

The chains flew once more and the Gadarene shouted yet louder: 'I…AM…NO…COWARD!'

'Revenge!' said Legion.

The Gadarene growled 'REVENGE!' Clenching his fists.

Slowly Legion now said 'I', drawing out the word.

The Gadarene closed his eyes and said 'I'.

'W i l l!' Legion spoke commandingly.

The Gadarene inhaled, held his breath and spoke: 'Will!'

'H a v e!'

Now the Gadarene spoke the word slowly, lowly, deliberately: 'H a v e!'

In unison both shouted: 'REVENGE!' The Gadarene opened his eyes. He swung his arms in unison, his hands holding the chains. They came crashing down together, and the tombstone was split in two. The Gadarene let out an ear-piercing wail. Legion was satisfied that he had all the dominion he needed to accomplish his purpose.

Unknown to Legion, a small boat landed at the shore of the Sea of Galilee. Thirteen men were disembarking not far away. A man in his early thirties was leading them.

Legion saw him at the same time the Gadarene did. At first the man was too far away to recognise, but that didn't concern the Gadarene. Here was a chance to release some of the rage, to begin his revenge.

The disciples had not been told the purpose of the trip, but many of them suddenly began to think that they would prefer not to stay very long. Running down the hill at them was a wild man. He was naked from head to foot and covered with dirt. His skin was bruised and gashed. His hair and beard were long and matted. His wrists were in manacles. There were chains in his hands. His breathing was heavy, growling, as he inhaled and exhaled and he had the eyes of a man with a fixed, and evil, purpose. The disciples began to fall back. Jesus alone stood his ground.

Legion's confidence was high. His dominion over the man and over his demons was ready for a test. Although he perceived the presence of angels, he wasn't concerned because of our subdued state.

The Gadarene continued to approach. A growl issued from deep in his chest. Finally, the Gadarene was within reach of Jesus. He drew back his right arm, chain in hand, and roared wildly. Legion, meanwhile, rose up to his full height. He manifested his darkened spirit and sought to provoke as much fear, horror and revulsion as he could, knowing that most men would recoil in dread before him. This would be his hour!

Jesus spoke, quickly, but fearlessly: 'I command you, you unclean spirit, come out of him!'

The Gadarene fell to his knees and elbows and began to shake. Slowly, he turned his head upward until he could just barely see the face of Jesus out of the corner of his eye. The spirit of terror had become a voice. It would still make most men cower in fear. Deep and halting, it spoke, trying to show its power, but al it could manage was: 'What - have - you, to do - with me—Jesus - Son - of - the - Most - High - God?'

Then the voice changed. It was desperate, almost human now, as it continued. 'I beg you, don't you torment me, too. Please, please don't torment me!'

Jesus continued to look directly at him, and spoke to the demon, 'You servant of Satan, what is your name?'

The response came from the deeper voice. 'My name is Legion, for we are many. We beg you, do not command us to return to hell.'

Legion continued. His voice was growing weaker. He begged. 'Send us away. Do not make us stay here with you. Send us into the herd of swine. They, too, are unclean, as we are. Send us there.'

Jesus responded, 'You may go.'

Immediately, they all left. None of them waited for a command from Legion, for his dominion over them was broken. None of them were eager to fight. They scattered throughout the herd, which then ran and drowned themselves in the sea rather than become hosts to the hellish horde.

"Michael," I asked, "what happened to the Gadarene?"

"He returned to his right mind immediately, although he was dazed and astonished. Very quickly he asked Jesus what had happened. Then, over the next few hours he repeatedly shook his head saying, 'What happened to me? I don't know who I am,…no, I know who I am! Finally!'

"Meanwhile, The herdsmen fled—some into in the city and some into the country—and told everyone what happened. The people of the village came to see for themselves. Only a few approached very closely. They still feared that the man would return to his previous state, even though they saw him sitting, in his right mind and fully clothed. Many of them were more afraid of Jesus than of the man. Finally some of them approached Jesus and asked him to depart with his disciples. Walking down to the boat with them, the Gadarene asked to go with them, but Jesus refused, saying to him, 'Go home to your friends, and tell them how much the Lord has done for you, and how he has had mercy on you.' It was necessary so that the people living in the Decapolis might believe. The Gadarene faithfully proclaimed how much Jesus had done for him, to the marvel of all."

"Well, you're right. The bible's account is much tamer than what really happened."

"So was mine."

"What do you mean? I thought you just…"

"I told you the story, but that does not mean you have experienced the reality. A spirit of hatred or cowardice can have amazing power. If you knew their power you would run from them—indeed you would run from every evil."

"Well, it's still an amazing story. I never imagined such a battle for a man's soul could take place."

"You have yet to hear about the most important battle for the souls of human beings."

"Which is…"

"Return tomorrow, Good Friday, at noon and we will continue. There are two stories you yet must hear. One is about a great battle, won in the past. The other will take place tomorrow. Now you must go and write what you have heard today."

I picked up my folder and began to walk away. Suddenly, the thought went through my mind to turn around. I wanted to see if Michael would walk away himself, or simply vanish in thin air. I turned and looked. He was still there, looking at me. He motioned with his hand to keep going. I turned again and left, mildly rebuked for my curiosity.

CHAPTER 5:

THE CROSS

Michael had not told me how many visitations there would be, but I was beginning to suspect that they wouldn't go beyond the weekend. When I arrived at the cathedral, I went to the Chapel of St. Michael. For the first time since our original meeting, he wasn't there. "Odd." I thought. I left the chapel and looked up the aisle to see if he was on his way. He wasn't. I turned to go back to the chapel, but then decided to look in the main nave of the cathedral. I scanned to the back but did not see him. Out of the corner of my eye I saw someone on the steps leading up to the high altar—a man kneeling on one knee. That would have been a bit forward in itself, but this man was dressed in the uniform of a first century Roman soldier—down to the sandals. It was Michael. He seemed to be praying. I wasn't sure whether to approach. After a moment I decided I would. I was sure it would become clear if this were inappropriate. As I approached, Michael seemed to finish. He stood and beckoned me. Being near to the sanctuary, I whispered when I spoke.

"Aren't you concerned that you might draw attention being dressed as you are, and kneeling here at the front of the cathedral?"

"No. It is you who should be concerned. I am invisible to all others except you. Anyone who is looking in this direction is looking at you and wondering why you are whispering into thin air."

I suddenly became quite self-conscious.

"Let's sit down," said Michael.

My attention was drawn to the figure of Christ hanging in death upon the large gold cross on the high altar. Michael was looking at it also as he asked me, "Do you remember the vision you had when you were praying? The one I mentioned to you in our first encounter."

"Yes, if it wasn't for that I would have ignored you as a whacko." Suddenly, the vision I had that Good Friday as I prayed came back to mind. "It was you! You were the angel I saw kneeling before the cross on that Good Friday."

"The vision you had was accurate. Today you will hear my account." With that, Michael began.

I am not the only witness of what happened. Mary or even the centurion could give you an account as well. But they were limited in what they saw. With human eyes they could not perceive what occurred in the spiritual realm. There were many more present on that day than they could see, and the part played by these others was no small one.

I have told you some about the ranks of the angels and you have seen something of the demonic, but there is more to tell about them. They, like us, vary in their powers and in their functions. All of them can tempt, just as all of us can worship. For most of them their primary role is to tempt and to harass human beings. Their level of power is low, but they can operate at incredible speed. That is their strength. They can sow the seed of doubt, hatred and lust among thousands very rapidly. Their work is usually experienced as a thought or a desire or an emotion. It is usually in the form of a temptation to do, or to say, or think something, and it can be very subtle. There were many of these spirits around that day.

Above them in rank are the demons who can gain special control over someone. This is usually spoken of as having an obsession or in the more noteworthy cases it is demonic possession. In these cases the ability of the individual to resist the suggestion made by the demon is greatly impaired. Such people have impulses that they cannot resist because, over time, they have yielded repeatedly to a temptation or they have entered into some agreement with an evil spirit.

What was noteworthy that Friday was the number of higher ranking officers in the horde who were there. Some of them were captains, who report to the commanders, who report to Satan himself. They rule over groups of demons known respectively as a mob, a throng and finally the whole horde of hell.

Captains have responsibility for the great cities and lesser nations. They often, intentionally, take a form that is grotesque or repulsive in order to evoke fear in their subordinates. It can destroy the confidence of lesser demons. Anger and hatred consume them. These are the key sources of their power. Through them they induce fear, and with enough fear, a subordinate can be made to do anything. Often the senior officers treat their allies with as much contempt as their enemies. Most of the senior officers control their subordinates as ruthlessly as Satan controls them.

Even so, under normal circumstances the demonic multitudes tremble in fear at my presence—but not that day. That day I, and the others with me, were ordered not to manifest our strength. We merely appeared in battle dress, our garments covered with the blood and grime of centuries of battle. Our subdued manner gave the horde unusual courage.

There is a hill outside the city walls of Jerusalem where the Romans customarily crucified the offenders against Roman law. Two men were already hanging from crosses. The Roman soldiers who had crucified them were now waiting for a third man to be crucified. Unseen and unheard by the Roman soldiers were two evil spirits who also were waiting in expectation of the third man to be crucified. As they waited, they began a conversation inaudible to human ears.

'Our mob captain is here.' A Spirit of Pride, was seeking to provoke a spirit of anger.

'I have already noted his obnoxious presence.'

'You have been pondering your tactics against him no doubt.'

'And would I tell you my plans, my dear Proud One? I know your ways. You would weasel information out of me and pass it on to our captain. Nice thought, but this time I will say nothing.'

The Spirit of Pride was hardly shaken that his ways were so obvious. Instantly, he changed his tactics. 'If I remember correctly, you nearly succeeded in defeating the captain last time. Nearly. Might I give you the help you need for your efforts to succeed.'

'Help? Pfff! From you? This time I have him. I know his weakness. I will succeed, and I don't need anyone's help, least of all yours. I will do it on my own. Last time I was promised help from slime like you, I got none and paid dearly for it. It was long before I recovered from the humiliation I received at the captain's hand. Last time I acted in foolish anger, but now I have regained my courageous hate. Soon I will have my revenge on him.'

The Spirit of Pride secretly congratulated himself on his success at provoking the Spirit of Anger to be proud. He continued his work. 'Still, your rebellion against our captain made you grow in wickedness. Surely you are now more wicked than he.'

'I could match him evil for evil...without doubt.'

'Are you not also now more wise?'

'Far wiser than him or you, you goad.' The Spirit of Anger was falling into the trap. His pride was growing; soon it would force him to act.

'Then why not act today?' The Spirit of Pride continued. 'He will be distracted by other important events today.'

'Why don't *you* act. You also hate him. Do you think I don't know that you want his position.'

'No,' the Spirit of Pride responded, 'today I will fight for the greater evil.'

'Do I detect loyalty to the Master of Hell?'

'No! Loyalty is beneath me. Even in its worst forms it has a touch of good. I will fight along with him today only because it is an opportunity to do the greater evil. Pride will again precede the fall.'

'You? I'm sorry my friend. You have no chance of getting our chief enemy to sin. I am playing a game I can win. You are doomed to lose.'

A little way off their mob captain was whispering into the ear of the Captain of the Roman Cohort.

'It has been a good while since you have had the pleasure of driving the spike, of feeling the warm blood. Perhaps today you should take over from your subordinates.'

'That is an odd thought,' reflected the Roman captain.

The demon continued. 'But possibly worthy of consideration…The job of directing this shoddy, contemptible cohort—what pleasure is there in that? You command others to do, but when do you get the pleasure of doing? Why not today? Why not be the one to inflict the punishment today.'

'It has been a while...'

The Captain of the Mob knew his man. Having sown the seed, he backed away. He walked toward his two subordinate demons, who were still in conversation, their backs toward him.

The Spirit of Pride saw the captain of their mob coming. He believed he knew what the Captain of the Mob had said to the Captain of the Roman Cohort—but why would the Captain of the Mob want to get the Roman captain to do the killing? Suddenly it was clear. There must be a reward from the master of darkness for the demon whose man crucified the Son of God. A new plan formed in his mind. He looked at the Spirit of Anger.

'Do you really think you can distract the Roman captain and undermine our mob captain's temptations?' The Spirit of Pride suggested to Anger.

'I have bigger plans than that.'

'Forget it. You can't succeed. Even if you get some centurion to kill the Roman captain it will backfire.'

'Did I say that was my plan?'

'What kind of fool are you. Do you think our captain won't find out?'

'Him?'

'Yes, him.'

'No chance. He's too stupid!'

'So you claim. But he may just be smart enough to assign you to work the crowd again. Poof, there go your plans.' The Spirit of Pride's goading was succeeding. The Spirit of Anger grew enraged. His darkness increased, but his powers of judgement shrank.

'Our captain. Hah! He'll never have a chance to assign me to anything. His mob rule will be broken. Today the captain will fall. I can match his strength. I have powers he has not yet seen. When Anger is unleashed beware. Today, the captain will...'

'Did I hear my name?' The voice was sarcastic. It belonged to the captain. The Spirit of Anger was caught and he knew it. 'Plotting again?' The captain continued. 'You fool.'

The Spirit of Pride backed away, having succeeded in the first part of his plot. He quickly slid over to the Captain of the Roman Cohort. 'You must be loyal to your position.' The Spirit of Pride also knew this man. 'Commanding is power. If you choose to do menial work, you will be given menial work. Who will fear you? You will be just another one of the men. You are a captain in the Roman army. Act like a general and you will become a general. Act like a mercenary and you will become a mercenary. Do not stoop to this menial task.'

Meanwhile, the Captain of the Mob stared at the Spirit of Anger, who stared back, considering a challenge, hardening his resolve, steeling his will. The captain held his stare, calmly concentrating his powers. The darkness around them grew. Then, slowly, the Spirit of Anger began to twist, one shoulder dropping and going forward, the other rising backward. Suddenly, he fell to the ground, broken.

'Not yet, fool! Go work the crowd. There are people to corrupt, and today it will be easy. Even you can do it. Many of them are already angry. Enrage them!' The captain kicked the Spirit of Anger and left.

Michael had paused.

"Do the subordinates ever succeed in their rebellion?" I asked.

"Seldom, even so they do rise up against those over them and unless they have managed to grow in their powers of evil, they lose, and when they do, they suffer for it. Thus, because it so seldom succeeds, there is less rebellion than there might be. Still, many try what is usually futile. The other reason they don't rebel as much as you might think is because losing a challenge against their superiors only leads to humiliation, and excruciating punishment, but it never leads to extinction."

"Why would that make a difference? I asked.

"They cannot fight to the death. There is no such thing as dying for the cause. There is no escape through death. Many human beings are willing to be martyrs. Who wants to be tortured forever? Death or extinction would be a relief for a demon but it never happens."

Michael continued.

The conversation I just recounted took place near the two men who had already been crucified. Next would be Jesus. The day was already heavily overcast, as he carried the transverse beam of the cross up the steep hill called Golgotha.

The bystanders were aware of an unusually great tension in the air. It was as if a fight were expected at any moment. The fiercest rivals from the armies of heaven and the hoards of hell were there, watching warily. Gabriel, Raphael and myself, plus many of our most capable warriors, had been sent to defend this man. Our enemy sought to destroy him. Both groups were completely invisible to the human eye, but many people sensed our presence, especially the malicious evil that accompanied the demonic horde. That day the glory of the angelic host was subdued and we were outnumbered by the great demonic horde that had gathered in Jerusalem to witness the confrontation between Jesus and Satan. Satan had boasted that he would put to death the Son of God. This was to be the hour of darkness.

Crucifixion is death of the most brutal kind, involving intense, unremitting pain for hours and humiliation before all who are looking on. Jesus was made to strip naked. The soldiers threw him to the ground and made him lie upon the transverse beam, arms outstretched. The entire horde drew near.

The Captain of the Roman Cohort approached his soldiers. The Captain of the Mob was at his ear. The Captain of the Roman Cohort picked up the hammer and the spikes and the Captain of the Mob whispered, 'Yes, do it yourself.'

But the Spirit of Pride was right there as well accompanying the soldier he had under his power. He spoke to the Captain of the Roman Cohort, 'Remember your pride!' Such a statement was a risk. The Spirit of Pride hoped it would be interpreted as a harmless statement by his mob captain, even as it prompted the Captain of the Roman Cohort to act as the Spirit of Pride desired. It worked. The Captain of the Roman Cohort handed the hammer and spikes to soldier assigned to the Spirit of Pride and said, 'You, take care of this.'

'Noooo!' said the Captain of the Mob, quickly shifting his glance to the Spirit of Pride, but there was nothing he could do. The Roman captain had decided.

Pride passed through the soldier with his darkness, assuming the exact form of the soldier as they knelt over the body of Jesus. The spike was put into place and with a mighty blow from the hammer, was driven home. Jesus clenched his teeth and held back the cry of pain.

The horde shouted for victory. Their darkness intensified. Pride, more than any other demon, grew in darkness. His thirst for evil

Michael Shaughnessy

increased as he moved his soldier in position to drive the second spike into place. 'Now I shall be mob-captain. Someday I will command a throng. I will have my revenge on every spirit who ever crossed me.' Pride again had triumphed.

'NOW!' He cried, and the soldier drove the second spike home. Again Jesus held back a cry of pain while the horde shouted in triumph.

'Yes!' Cried one the throng-leaders. 'The rescuer of men is now the hostage of hell.'

To that it was not easy to listen. The desire of the heavenly host was to hear an immediate call to war. One after another my finest warriors came up to me pleading, 'This can't be right. Give us the order to fight for his honour and stop this shame!'

As the commander of the heavenly host I responded. 'I too desire to draw the sword, to speak the truth, to drive out the darkness, but our orders are to wait, to watch and to act only if commanded. Brothers, our zeal for righteousness must be tempered by our obedience. Our commands are clear. We must wait.'

Standing off by themselves, were Mary and some of the other women who were followers of Jesus. They could get no closer due to the many soldiers and Jewish leaders gathered near the cross. Even so they could still hear the groans of agony from those who had been crucified.

The Roman soldiers now finished their task. Using ropes they raised the crucified Jesus on the transverse beam and secured it to the vertical beam. A footrest had already been secured to upright beam. Jesus feet were set upon it. One was placed over the other and a spike was driven through them both. The crucifixion was complete.

A young scribe had drawn back when the final spike was driven through the feet of Jesus. He saw the look of pain and the flow of blood and turned away. Immediately a demon was at his side. 'The lesson is necessary.'

The scribe pushed his way through the crowd, leaving. The demon followed him. 'The people will only learn if the point is firmly made. Blasphemy must be firmly punished or people will not believe.'

The scribe continued, undeterred, thinking to himself, 'If the people do not believe, they do not believe. Deterrents to sin do not produce faith.' The demon fell away and returned to the crowd seeking others to tempt.

One of the chief priests caught Jesus' attention. He was prodded by another mob captain who stood behind him. 'Are you not the Messiah, the Saviour of the whole world? How long we have waited for your appearing to save us from our misery filled lives! But you can't even save yourself!...Oh, we're ready to follow you. Show us your power that we might become true believers. Come, lead us!' He threw back his head and laughed heartily, full of self-satisfaction.

The mob captain spoke with delight as he noted how easily the chief priest could be stirred to act. 'This one will be of use to me. He thoroughly trusts himself. Yet how little he knows that I am the source of his most brilliant thoughts! Who was it that prompted him to shout, "Crucify him! Crucify him!" just in time to save the trial before Pilate? Yes I will use this man.'

Prodded again by the mob captain, the chief priest dropped his chin, looked out the top of his eyes and spoke in mockery. 'So, you're going to destroy the temple and rebuild it in three days! That would be a mighty act! Let's see it.'

A slithery spirit of self-righteousness crept up behind the chief priest and congratulated him. 'What a fool this Jesus is! It is good that you saved these poor wretches from following such a lunatic. The slime of your people can never tell what is true and good. They will follow anyone.'

Like so many of the demons, his voice was harsh and grating to our ears but in the minds of men it sounded strong yet mild. The chief priest nodded to himself, noting how good and helpful he had been in preventing the rabble from making the great mistake of following this Jesus.

Jesus quietly quoted the scriptures.

'More in number than the hairs of my head are those who hate me without cause. Mighty are those who would destroy me, those who attack me with lies...I have become an alien to my brethren...The insults of those who are insulting you have fallen upon me. My knees are weak. My body has become gaunt. I am an object of scorn to my accusers, when they see me, they wag their heads.'

Focussing his thoughts helped him to not yield to crying out in agony.

Once again I listened for the voice of the Most High, hoping for a word, a signal that we could intervene, and still, none came.

Thunder rumbled in the distance. The sky grew darker and the air grew heavier. Among my men there was an increased awareness of evil. They searched for something, someone. They suspected who, but knew not where. Many were listening intently, trying to pick up more clearly whatever it was they were sensing. The demonic horde at first grew restless, then anxious and fearful. Many were wincing as if in pain. Others were looking for a place to hide.

Then I saw him, a commander of a throng, a spirit of hatred and murder bearing great authority. Commanders normally spread themselves over entire nations. This one, however, had concentrated his darkness greatly, taking a disfigured human form 9 feet tall. His visage was so repulsive even his own captains found it difficult to look at him. I knew him before he had fallen but now I could hardly recognise him. He had fallen so far. He had been a creature of beauty, inspiring to look at, but now he was so disfigured that I shuddered in horror at what he had become.

The spirit of hatred and murder approached Jesus from behind the cross, so as to whisper over Jesus' shoulder. His voice was convincing. It was the same voice that had incited Cain to murder his brother Abel. His reasoning had been impeccable. It had made the conclusions of his counsel easy to follow and seem utterly devoid of wrong. Yet every trace of love in his heart he had personally mutilated beyond all recognition. In its place he had cultivated a deep hatred for all that is good. He could brook no compassion or mercy if he were to succeed in this temptation. Even so, his voice was smooth and confident. 'Those worthless high priests. They are filled with self-righteousness. Jesus, how right you were when you called them whitewashed tombs. They deserve everything they will get. They deserve no mercy. As David foretold, "*Let them be blotted out of the book of the living!*"

The commander signalled to the captain, who again prompted the chief priest to rail at Jesus. 'You're a charlatan, a fool, a misguided egomaniac. I have seen neither humility nor courage in you. But I should not be surprised. I have not seen wisdom, justice, or any sign of the Spirit of God at work in you either!' Then he turned to the crowd and continued, 'This man is in league with the devil himself.'

Again Jesus recalled the words of the Psalm,

'Wicked and deceitful mouths are opened against me, speaking against me with lying tongues. They beset me with words of hate and attack me without cause. In return for my love they accuse me, even as I make prayer for them. So they reward me evil for good, hatred for my love.'

The commander of the throng turned to Jesus. 'Tell him off. Tell off this lying fool. He has blasphemed the Holy Spirit. You must judge him. Now!...Put him in his place. Exercise your righteous wrath!'

Closing his eyes, Jesus spoke. 'Father, forgive this man. Forgive him. He doesn't know what he's doing.'

Jesus' words shattered the false calmness of the Spirit of Hatred and Murder. 'Forgive him! No, never forgive!' The commander grew darker in countenance and his voice grew in intensity. Now he moved directly in front of the cross and rebuked Jesus to his face with a commanding voice. 'Where is your justice, oh you righteous judge? These chief priests are false and treacherous men. They claim to be holy. They claim to be honest. They claim to know the truth but they are liars, murderers and thieves. Do you call this justice? Justice??? They mislead your followers and you do nothing! Where is your loyalty to the truth?

Where is your courage in upholding what is right? Where is your justice, if you are to judge the nations? These priests deserve to be condemned! Strike them down!' NOW!

Jesus stared back at the commander, but refused to respond. In anger the commander turned to two lesser demons who were gloating at his defeat. He hit them across the face with the back of his hand and ordered them, pointing to the thieves, 'Break these two men!'

One man was to the left of Jesus and the other to the right. Periodically they would steel themselves, and press their bodies upward to relieve the pain in their shoulders, arms and hands, invariably reopening the wounds in their feet. This agony however gave no substantial relief and after a few moments they dropped back down and let out another long, deep groan, knowing that this agonising torture could last for days.

The two demons had already been testing the two men, pressing them to the final stages of corruption. They had captured their hearts long ago. Now the Spirit of Bitterness called up some old memories and distorted them further. Each thought was a poison tipped barb.

The first thief pressed his body upward so he could take a deeper breath. Through his clenched teeth, he tried to speak. This too was painful. He turned his head toward Jesus. Although his voice was weak, his spite was clear. 'Aren't you the Christ? Save yourself.

Save us. Aren't you the Saviour of the Jews? Well, we're Jews, so save us.' He exhaled but refused to drop back down. Again he drew a breath. His bitterness grew. 'Some king you are. Where is your power? Where are your armies? You're no king. Death will soon reign over you just as it will over us.' With that he spat at him, then exhaled, took another breath and in dropping down again, he exhaled and groaned.

The second thief had been under the dominion of a spirit of self-importance for years. The demon had succeeded in making the man more vain and foolish with every successful crime he committed. Each failure had been attributed to the stupidity of his fellow thief.

Once again this spirit of self-importance crawled into the mind of the thief and spoke his crooked advice. 'This is your last chance for revenge. Take it out on this Jew. He's a hypocrite, false like those who betrayed you. Now is your chance. He is just like the ones who put you here: scum who claim to rule over you. This one has even claimed to be a king. Make this self-proclaimed king a fool. Drag him down from his lofty pride. Subject him to the same abuse that you have had to endure. You are the equal of any man. You have nothing to fear from this 'king'. What can he do nailed to that cross, dying?'

For once the second thief did not hear what he had been told. The unremitting pain had been an inescapable focus since he had been crucified. But something had happened a moment earlier, which jolted him out of his pain. He saw how Jesus had shown forgiveness, sincere forgiveness, for the very chief priest who had been persecuting him. Now he was thinking for himself for the first time in years. 'What kind of man is this? How can he show mercy? How can he forgive? Who other than a king would act with nobility such as this...? But he cannot be an ordinary king.' Suddenly, the pain returned full force.

The second thief groaned. The pain in his upper torso and arms was again becoming unbearable. The extension of his arms, lungs and diaphragm made breathing very difficult. He hiked himself up on the footrest and drew in a breath of air. He turned his head toward Jesus and then looked past him to the first thief. Haltingly, he spoke to his co-criminal. 'You're wrong.' He exhaled and took a short breath. With less movement there was less pain. 'We are punished justly. He is not.' Again he caught a short breath. He looked at Jesus. 'My Lord,...remember me...when you come into your kingdom.' He could not hold this position any longer. He exhaled and dropped back down. His head fell forward, his chin touching his chest.

Immediately, the Spirit of Self-importance responded with an assault of doubt. The man had escaped his grip. 'What kind of kingdom will this man have? Look at him. His hope is gone. There will be no last minute rescue. His life is already all but spent. He will have no messianic kingdom here. You will find no salvation coming from him. Any hope you put in him is false. Only a fool would follow him. Don't throw away your pride by clinging to this empty lie.'

Due to the scourging before his crucifixion, Jesus was already very weak. He turned his head what little he could. It was just enough for their eyes to meet. He spoke softly, very slowly. 'I tell you the truth. Today you will be with me in paradise.'

The words pierced in the heart of the second thief, instantly convincing him. He thought, 'That voice is truth.' For the Spirit of Self-importance it was as though he had been touched with hot iron. He leapt back from the thief, but refused to give up. He approached again, attempting to enter the mind of the second thief but a barrier of light and truth had gone up and his access was gone.

Another chief priest approached Jesus. He was even angrier because of the reference to Jesus' kingship. Pilate had a title inscribed over the cross, 'Jesus of Nazareth, King of the Jews.' This chief priest had demanded that Pilate remove the inscription, but Pilate refused, saying, 'What I have written will stand written.' He didn't realise that what he had written was true and would stand written for all time. A spirit of spite had inspired Pilate to do it to mock the Jews, and also made him refuse to change it. Now the chief priest sought to prove the inscription wrong. 'If he is the King of Israel, let him come down from that cross! He trusts in God. Let God deliver him.'

The commander of the horde approached Jesus again. 'You do have the power to come down from that cross. The chief priest doesn't know it, but I do, and so do you. This is not necessary. We can make a deal. I will give to you the souls you desire. We don't need them all. We don't even want them all. In any case, the thief was right. This is unjust punishment. Why endure it? Leave it behind. This race is not worth such suffering. There must be another way than this.'

Jesus ignored him. 'I thirst.' He said and quietly quoted the psalm: *'Insults have broken my heart, so that I am in despair…'*

'Then come down and drink.' The commander spoke with tempting consolation. Jesus again gave no response. At this the Captain of the Mob approached one of the soldiers. 'Give him a sponge filled with vinegar to drink!'

Jesus continued, *'I looked for pity, but there was none; and for comfort but none could be found. They gave me poison for food and for my thirst they gave me vinegar to drink.'*

At that, Raphael rose to his feet. In the garden of Gethsemane, he had been assigned to bring Jesus strength and consolation as he chose to do his Father's will. 'I want to help him.' Raphael said. 'No man should carry such a burden alone.' Both thieves were groaning now louder than before. 'Michael…' he said turning toward me. He did not finish the question he began. Instead he lifted his eyes toward heaven and listened. His answer was instant and clear. He was not to intervene, not this time. The cup of suffering had to be drunk. Today he was not to bring any comfort, minister no food nor drink, no light nor life.

Gabriel, the great messenger, was also with us. He also wanted to intervene. 'Even just a few words…' But Gabriel's orders were also clear. 'You, servant of the Word, kneel and watch. Your words of truth and hope you must not speak. This is his final test. You must say nothing.' Like me, Gabriel and Raphael did not yet understand the full will of the Most High but we knew our orders and obeyed.

The taunting and the lying continued around us. Another commander of a throng had wrapped himself around the right arm of the cross. He spoke. 'You have failed. Where is your following? Your offer of salvation has been refused. Peter denied you. Judas betrayed you. Thomas doesn't believe you. Your training of these men was wasted. And where are all those you were supposed to convert? They have abandoned you. Where are all those you healed? They don't care! Where are all these angels who are supposed to bear you up on eagles wings? Look! They tremble in fear before our great might. No, you have no following, no support. There is no future for you or these so-called disciples. It all ends, here, now! You are a failure, an irresponsible, incompetent failure.'

Gabriel prayed quietly. 'Father, these are lies. We do not tremble before them. Let me help. What man can hold out against this? You have never before allowed a man to contend unaided with these our greatest enemies. We have always been sent to help. These are the ruthless: captains, commanders!' Gabriel waited, but no answer came. We knew it meant his appeal was rejected. He was not to intervene.

Suddenly Raphael spoke: 'Look…' All around Jesus the darkness was increasing, even though the demons had not drawn any closer. The weight of the darkness settled upon his shoulders. His head bowed further toward his chest. 'What form of evil is this?'

We waited. Searching, sensing…'Sin and guilt?' I said.

'Yes, certainly, but it is more. This is too thick, too heavy.'

'It is shame and bondage as well.' I said. The evil was quickly becoming oppressive.

'I have never seen them combined this way—all together at once. Something is not right here.' Raphael was deeply worried.

The darkness grew yet thicker.

'And now destruction, disease and death…It is every evil I have ever fought.' He added. 'But that is an impossible burden. No man can carry that.'

This was the hour of my temptation. I have a will tempered to fight. It is fierce, unbending, unyielding to anyone or anything but the Most High himself. I was ready to draw my sword, to enter this fight, to defend the right. I knelt on one knee before the cross, my forehead resting on the handle of my sheathed sword and prayed. 'Father, speak but the word. I am a warrior. This is my purpose, my calling. If ever there was a time for battle, surely it must be now. This is the time to defeat your foes and the foes of men.' But the divine silence continued. We were not to intervene.

All around us, it grew yet darker. A great clap of thunder sounded. The sense of evil grew yet more oppressive. Men and women, without knowing why, bent their heads and pulled up their hoods, hiding and shielding themselves. All the heavenly host were turning their heads away and closing their eyes.

I forced myself to face what I knew was coming. I alone had ever been entrusted with the strength to stay the hand of Satan himself, though I was never permitted to destroy him. We have fought in Persia, in Russia and throughout the earth. Numerous times my master has called upon me to prevent Satan from accomplishing his works of terror and war. A righteous anger burns in me against him. I can tolerate neither his blasphemy nor his malice. My will steeled itself to destroy him and his work, once and for all. I knew the signs. Satan himself was on his way.

Now even the captains and commanders shuddered with terror. Their already disfigured faces twisted and distorted further. The demonic horde grew more agitated. Involuntarily the lesser demons' arms and legs became grotesquely contorted. Elbows and knees were disjointed and bent backwards. Hands became gnarled and arthritic. Necks were bent. Heads were twisted. The despot of hell hardened his tyranny over each of his minions.

I looked up at Jesus. His head was lifted. His eyes were attentive, his concentration sharp. After a pause he whispered, 'He is here. This is the hour when darkness reigns.'

Rolling thunder sounded in the ears of men. In reality it was the deep appalling laugh of the Prince of Darkness. Long, low, and mocking, again and again, the scornful laugh thundered. Now Satan's moment had come, and he spoke. 'Behold weakness incarnate. This is your god? Powerless, weak, and helpless. Your god is crippled by love—for fools!'

I rose. With force I whispered under my breath, 'No! No more! Your hatred and malice shall not be without limit. This must end! Father!' I cried. My hand went to my sword in order to be ready, but I was stopped in the act of drawing it. The command was firm: my sword must remain sheathed. I was not to defend his life. I was not to lift my hand against the enemy. I was to watch and wait until the Son of the Most High finished his work. I was told we would not act until full atonement was made, until justice was satisfied, until the suffering was complete. A mortal blow would be struck before we would be given permission to intervene.

'Yes, my Lord.' I responded. I bowed and knelt once more.

Again I heard the vile voice of the Prince of Darkness. 'Now you will see my real power over this race. I led them into sin and you are powerless to lead them out. Every one of them has rejected you. You are neither their redeemer nor their friend. You cannot save them. They are mine. And you, you who were so foolish as to join yourself to them, you too will now be mine. Hades shall be your home forever. You too must die.' His words were putrefying. They were like maggots on a seeping carcass—repulsive, horrid.

Everyone present felt the temperature drop. Men and women began to shiver. An oily blackness seemed to ooze over the body of Jesus, drawing all the remaining warmth from his body.

Now Jesus lifted himself high upon the cross, inhaled deeply and cried out,

My God, my God, why have you abandoned me? Why are you so far from helping me, from the words of my groaning? Oh my God, I cry by day but you do not answer; and by night but find no rest...'

111

Under his breath, such that only I could hear, Gabriel said 'Do not give in to their lies. Do not give in!' With great effort, Gabriel held his tongue. In the midst of this near total darkness, Jesus was being tempted to believe that his Father had forsaken him.

The hideous voice continued. 'Even the one who has sent you has abandoned you, just as he has abandoned your race. He can see they are vermin. They are nothing like him. They are like me. They love sin in all its morbidity: lust, lies, betrayal and murder. This is the eternity they have chosen. And now you too have been forsaken. Your spirit is in my hands. Your eternity will be under *my* dominion. The Light from Light is now to be quenched forever. You will be tramped underfoot until you are nothing more than the cold, black mud of hell. Your neck will be my footstool!' Satan turned his eyes toward heaven and with clenched fist he demanded: 'GIVE ME HIS LIFE!'

Jesus was now in his final moments of suffering. As I watched, I trembled. 'Is this how it ends?' I asked. I could not believe that the Most High would abandon the human race and I certainly could not see how in all justice, he could abandon Jesus.

Only then did the Most High draw back the veil shrouding his will. Sin had come into the world through one man and with sin, death. The one man's disobedience had lead to condemnation for all. Now one man's obedience unto death, even death on a cross, would lead to acquittal and life for all who call upon his name in faith. No great army of angels would slay the power of sin, loose the chains of death, and shatter the bars of hell. It would be the work of a man, this man, crippled by love for fools.

The mortal blow to be struck suddenly became clear, but Satan would not be the one to strike it. This was to be a blow against death and sin, and Jesus was about to strike them down forever—triumphing over death by death, his own death, freely given, one man's life for the lives of all men. Yes, Satan was to be defeated, but not by me, not by the host of heaven, not even by the Most High, but by this man, this son of man, the Son of God. Oh, the depths and richness of the wisdom and knowledge of the Most High! How unsearchable are his judgments and how inscrutable his ways!

Jesus grew weaker. He no longer had even the strength to breathe. A minute passed. The scourging had taken his strength and now the crucifixion was taking his life. Another minute passed. I watched Jesus open his eyes. In them I saw his love, love for all humanity, but even more, I saw love for his Father and joy in doing his Father's will. One last time, with the last of his strength he raised himself up and inhaled. He lifted his eyes and said, 'It...is finished,' and yielded his spirit back into the hands of his

Father. The body dropped, hanging by its arms and his head fell to his chest.

I waited for Michael to continue, and then wondered whether to say something. Michael had done more than recount the story. I felt that in telling it he had somehow nearly re-lived it. For a few moments neither of us moved. Then Michael looked into the nave of the cathedral. People were arriving for the afternoon liturgy. "You must go and take your seat for the Good Friday service. Once it has ended, return."

CHAPTER 6:

THE VIGIL

The recounting of the passion and death of Jesus Christ as it was sung from the Gospel of John was more real to me than I can ever remember. The service lasted nearly two hours and was standing room only. It ended in silence.

I waited for the crowd to depart so I could return to the Chapel of St Michael. I recollected what Michael had unfolded of the events of Good Friday and found myself growing angry at the injustice and insolence of Satan in demanding the life of the Lord. That the wicked could triumph and then gloat, especially in such an evil act! I had to ask Michael when I returned. He made it easy for me.

"You may ask whatever you would like."

"Michael, was there a victory celebration in hell? Did Satan rejoice in putting the Lord to death?"

"No. A celebration would imply joy. Satan has lost his capacity for any true joy. He has fallen too far."

"Didn't he think he had triumphed over Jesus by putting him to death? Did he gloat?"

"It is a bit hard to say."

Michael saw the surprised look on my face. I explained, "I wasn't expecting that answer. You seem to have known everything about Satan so far. Do you mean there is something you don't know about him?"

"There is much that I do not know about him. Not that it is forbidden. It is just that it is not wise. I too could become fascinated with evil. The study of Satan is a dangerous thing. I guard my mind against it. Remember, he was created more powerful than I. I still don't know how much of that power he has lost. I only do battle with him as I am commanded. When commanded, I expect grace will be provided to win— unless the will of the Most High is that I should lose. So far that has never been his will.

"…But I digress. The question was, 'Didn't he think he had triumphed over Jesus by putting him to death?' Not really.

"The wail that was heard at Satan's fall from heaven was not just the pain of separation from the Most High and thus from love, truth and beauty. It was more. Satan realised with utter clarity and finality, the foolishness of his attempt to grasp power from the hand of the Most High. Yet, he has lived willfully in misery and hopelessness since. He has known all along that, eventually, he will be completely and eternally defeated. He has never had any hope of victory."

I interrupted with a question. "Wait a minute. Michael, didn't you say Satan hoped to successfully tempt Jesus in the wilderness. That is what he said to those demons that were with him, if I remember correctly."

"Unfortunately, you don't. I quoted Satan as saying, 'Do you think I tempt because I have a hope of success?' The correct meaning of these words is not exactly as they would appear. Remember Satan's nature. Satan is the deceiver. He is a liar and the Father of Lies. He was deceiving his own servants. He didn't mean 'Do you think I have only a *hope* of success? No, I am certain of it.' That is what he intended his subordinates to believe, but Satan did not tempt Jesus because he believed he would succeed, he tempted Jesus because he is evil and hates what is good. His pride makes him unwilling to admit to defeat, even though he knows it is inevitable. When he tempted Jesus, his motivation was anger and hatred. Satan had no hope of victory. He acts out of a calculated, and blind rage."

"Back up again. You said—a calculated and blind rage. Isn't that a contradiction in terms?"

"No. Satan calculates every move, so that his motivation will be as purely evil as he can make it. Yet, it is blind to all other motivation, intentionally so. That is why his own salvation is out of the question. He refuses every good that he can. He has refused every offer of a merciful pardon. Mercy is good, so he has rejected it. He will never receive it no matter how often it is offered to him. His pride is far too great to consider receiving mercy. Even to hope for mercy is, for him, a sign of weakness. No, in hell there is no hope—no hope of things improving. There is no hope even of things not getting any worse. There is *no* hope.

"Dante says there is a sign over the entrance to hell which says, 'Abandon all hope ye who enter here.' Is there such a sign?"

"There is no need for a sign. You don't abandon hope when you enter hell—it abandons you. An empty, devouring darkness invades the soul. That is followed by an absolute conviction that this darkness is forever. You don't need a sign to tell you, you know it as certainly as you have ever known anything before. Hell is hopeless. There was certainly no hope of victory on Satan's part, he knows he is defeated."

"Then why was Satan so interested in seeing Jesus put to death?"

"I can give two answers. The first has to do with Satan's reasoning. He refused to believe that the Most High would allow humanity's salvation to come through the death of Jesus. And second, death meant consignment to Hades, the realm of the dead. A realm where Satan believed he alone reigned. He was convinced that through death Jesus too would be under his dominion. I doubt he would have put him to death otherwise."

"Does that mean that God tricked him?"

"No. The Most High simply acted according to his plan from the beginning of time. Satan acted according to his self-perverted nature in response. In the crucifixion he could only see evil; he couldn't see love. That is the second reason Satan was so interested in seeing Jesus put to death. He is different than we are. We have an infinite desire for love, both to give it and to receive it. Satan has corrupted this. In him it is a nearly infinite capacity for hate. This is why he does all that he does and hate, in its purest form, brings no delight. Many people hate others and they gain a perverted delight from the act of hating. They have a self-love that is somehow gratified by the destruction of anything good. They gloat saying, 'I showed them!' But Satan hates because it is now his nature. There is no gratification in it for him at all. As the Most High can say, 'I am,' so Satan says 'I hate.' He doesn't feel exalted by dragging down the good. He seeks to destroy the good simply because it is good. That is why he sought to destroy Jesus. That is why he seeks to destroy you. That is why he seeks to destroy all that is good. He hates it. He hates his own Creator. He hates me. He hates you. He hates all human beings. He hates his own minions, and finally, he hates, loathes, despises, even himself and everything he has done."

"If he hates all that he has done, wouldn't that mean he regrets what he has done?...Or at least the consequences of what he has done."

"No. To regret would mean thinking it better to have done something differently. This he refuses to do. Regret can be the first step to repentance, the desire to change one's ways. For him there can be no repentance. He has chosen this falsehood: that his way, the way of hatred, is perfect."

"That means he can't fail." I added.

"In his terms, yes. Exactly. He cannot fail. In every action he undertakes, he either accomplishes the evil he set out to do, in which case he is successful but cannot take any joy in it. Or when he doesn't accomplish the evil he set out to do, he falls back onto self-hatred. In all he does, he either ends by hating others or hating himself. In either case there is no failure, no regret. In the end he will have no authority or power left. Even then he will not repent. He will simply have a pure and total hate just for himself—an amazing form of self-centredness. Self-hatred will consume him and he will consume it. His end will be total self-derision.

"...If only your race understood the future. The end they face is to be like him or to be like Christ. Their outcome will be one or the other. If they do not explicitly decide to be like Jesus, they will eventually become like Satan. Those are the only two options."

119

"It seems to me that almost no one would explicitly choose to be like Satan, would they?"

"You didn't listen closely enough. This isn't a choice for one or the other. The choice is not option 'A' or option 'B'. You need to choose option 'A'. If you don't, you will automatically receive option 'B'."

"I would have thought it might be the other way around. That if you don't choose for evil, you will automatically receive the good. If you don't choose for hell, you automatically receive heaven."

"Many people think that way. Unfortunately they are wrong. Heaven is a place of absolute, untainted good. This good must be chosen. Simply put, not to choose this good is to make a profoundly evil choice. To make it even clearer, answer this question. For heaven to be heaven what must it be like?"

"A place of goodness? A place of happiness? A place of freedom?...Am I close?"

"Very, yet you missed by an infinity and eternity or two."

"Huh?"

"Heaven is a place of *infinite and eternal* goodness, *infinite and eternal* happiness and *infinite and eternal* freedom. Goodness and happiness are not forced upon you. They must be chosen, freely chosen."

"Well, that makes it easy, then. Who wouldn't choose to be happy?"

"Many, and for two reasons. First, happiness and goodness are inseparable. If you want to be happy you must also choose for good and not just a form of good but the greatest good. That is difficult for fallen creatures like yourself, but secondly, and more importantly, choosing for this necessitates choosing for the *source* of infinite and eternal happiness and goodness."

"It's like electricity. If you aren't plugged into the source, you don't get the power."

"That is a good analogy. Now answer this 'What is the source of infinite and eternal good?'"

"I suppose it must be something infinitely and eternally good—like God!"

"Exactly. The Most High is the creator, the source of all that is good, beautiful and true."

"A bit obvious, now I suppose."

"Yet many people believe something quite foolish indeed. Something like: 'I have the power to make myself happy forever.'"

"But if that is true, why hasn't anybody done it by now? That would be a big seller: true and eternal goodness—the latest happy meal from McJollies."

"No one has done it because it is impossible. How can a finite being, bring itself infinite and eternal happiness. It can't. It's that simple. A finite object cannot fill an infinite space."

"I cannot be my own end."

"And not to put too fine a point on it, during this life you either choose for the infinite good or for something less, and that is what you get in the next life: more and more of the infinite good or less and less of him."

"It does puzzle me a bit."

"What?"

"That although some people have no time or interest in God in this life, they somehow think that in the next life they will think differently."

"Not just differently, but the opposite!"

"Michael, returning to the original area of inquiry, if there wasn't a victory celebration in hell, what was there?"

"More of what had always been there, only now even worse: tyranny, hatred, criticism, deceit, despair...This is the fruit of rejecting the Most High. It was even worse because the mercy of the cross, the opportunity for reconciliation between heaven and hell, had now been completely rejected.

"Even so, this was not a time of rest for them. Satan saw it as a prime opportunity for sowing seeds of doubt, despair, self-condemnation and any other foul thoughts he could. The disciples were as susceptible as they had ever been since answering the original call. Herod and the Sanhedrin were assigned demons to harden them in their enmity toward the disciples. Pilate was wishing he could be rid of it all, but to wash the hands is not to wash the soul. The Sanhedrin allowed him no peace until he approved guards for the tomb."

Michael paused again. He looked up in thought at the gold leaf mosaic overhead and then turned toward me. "Time is running out. We must move on. Earlier, I said there were two stories you must hear. The first one I have recounted in part already: the battle of Jesus Christ with Satan. The second one I will tell you now...Do you remember the young woman you saw on the underground Wednesday?"

"The one dressed in black with a head like a pin-cushion? Yes, I ran into her again yesterday at lunch!" I responded.

"Yes. Her name is Kathleen McDonnell, although she normally goes by the name Kate."

"Yes, Kate. I heard her name."

"I am observing Kathleen's case, and how it is being conducted."

"What do you mean? Is she on trial? Is that what her sister Fiona was concerned about?"

"In a manner of speaking, yes. Like everyone, her soul is on trial and that is what her sister is concerned about."

Michael went on to fill me in on her background. "Her story is not uncommon in these days. Kathleen is from Belfast. Like many from there, she originally came to London looking for work. Her older sister, Fiona, had preceded her. Fiona and Kathleen were raised in a religious home, that started her well on the path of faith, but it wasn't enough. We have had to fight hard for her soul the last five years. Right now she is at a very decisive point in her life. I fear she has given up, but we will still fight to the very end."

"Do you know what the outcome will be in her case?"

"No, I only know what the Most High reveals, and this he has not revealed to me. Her life and soul both hang in the balance. What she does today may determine her eternal fate. She is seriously considering suicide."

"Really? I know that happens, I just don't…"

"It does happen and it is always a tragedy. Pray it does not happen tonight. If it does, I am afraid you will see it."

I inhaled deeply, shocked by how serious the situation with this woman was and then even more shocked by the thought of witnessing a suicide. "I couldn't let her do that!"

"You won't be in a position to prevent it."

I didn't know how to respond. I also was surprised that Michael seemed to ignore my internal reaction. He simply continued.

"I haven't the time to give the whole history of the battle for her soul. That would take too long, but I will give you the most important details. As I said, Kathleen was brought up in a fairly strong Christian home where all seven children were sent off to church each week, but that was where 'religion' ended. It was something Kate saw only as a duty. At 16 and 15 respectively, Fiona and Kate were close. They would talk about everything. That summer they went away together on a youth retreat. Fiona met the Lord quietly one evening and it changed her. Kate had what she later termed her 'religious experience.' It changed her as well, but for the worse."

"That sounds strange. How could it change her for the worse?" I was relieved to be simply following the story again and not thinking about a potential suicide.

"After the weekend Kate came down from her emotional high. Some of what she experienced was just religious hype with no real content, so she rejected the whole experience as a sham."

"Was it?"

"Not all of it." Michael responded, shrugging his head and shoulders. "The Most High was reaching out to her in spite of the hype.

"Anyway, this marked the beginning of a slide her life took. She changed her friends in reaction and joined in with a set of girls who identified themselves as 'the misfits'. She made every effort to be accepted by them, which included turning violently against what little faith she still had. It was a major setback for her, and for us. We have been working hard to bring her back."

"Have you appeared to her, too?"

"No." Michael shook his head. "There were no appearances, but she has been spoken to."

"By you? How?"

"No, not by me, rather in much the same way as you and all others are spoken to—angels of comfort, her guardian angel. Angels of comfort are generally under the command of Gabriel and Raphael. The guardian angels are under my command because they are the warriors, guardians. These are the ones who prompt your conscience to do what is right, and help defend against all manner of temptation. If you listened carefully you might well be able to distinguish your guardian's voice from the voice of your conscience. In a few moments you will see her warrior, her guardian. He is called Teshua. He has spoken to her often, of late however, she has refused to listen. But let me return to Kate's story."

Now Michael stood up and gently paced as he continued his narrative.

"Her first years in London she had everything she wanted. She had a job as a model, earned very good money and was, as she puts it, 'being seen with the right people'. Being accepted by others, especially the elite was an obsession. Appearance was very important. She bought expensive clothes, went to the most popular clubs, and spent large sums on her hair, nails and make-up."

"That's something I just don't understand."

"You're not a woman." He answered, pointing his finger and giving me a knowing look, then continuing. "...With it all came a dissolute lifestyle. I'll spare you the details and preserve her modesty."

"Even though she didn't?" I interrupted. Michael turned and looked directly at me.

"Especially because she didn't." He turned away and continued.

"Eventually, her understanding of right and wrong deteriorated. Her mind grew more and more confused. She began to take risks with her life, not to mention her soul. In the process she developed anorexia nervosa."

"Michael, this seems like a Hollywood story, not reality. It's a bit over-dramatic, don't you think?" I tried to catch his eye, but his gaze was that of one whose mind is preoccupied.

"No." he replied. "We could be looking in on hundreds of cases tonight in this city alone that are more 'dramatic' if that's what you want to call it. To a young woman who was sexually abused by her neighbour, the sexual abuse is not drama. It is her personal experience. The same is true for the young boy whose mother is a prostitute with a heroin addiction or even the upper-middle-class banker who is about to have a fatal stroke. The drama is exactly the same."

"I guess it's just that my life seems to have so little pain or drama in comparison." I said.

"Pain, yes. Drama, no. The drama is the same for all human beings."

"Sorry, I got us off the subject again." I wanted to ask about the drama bit, but thought I was diverting the conversation too much as it was.

Michael continued. His narrative style was simple. He stated the facts without emphasis, without emotion. "Her guardian angel, Teshua made an added effort at this point. Often in weakness people see spiritual reality more clearly. Teshua convinced her that even her body was rejecting her lifestyle. Instead of turning around she began working harder, eating less. Drugs were the next step in attempting to cope. Finally, she knew she needed help. She thought maybe a more permanent relationship might do it, but her choice in the matter wasn't very good—she moved in with a cocaine dealer. Her cycle of emotions grew even more erratic. Her dealer managed to get her to crave his affirmation even while he seldom gave it. She remained in the relationship for two years until she realised she was constantly being degraded. Finally, she left, more lost and broken...Again Teshua intervened. Kate very nearly decided to reform at this point. She knew she didn't like her life and needed a real change."

"What happened?"

"Something that often happens with human beings. Small things can have big consequences. Kate was invited to visit a friend who lived in Amsterdam. She hoped this was the opportunity for change she needed. It was another disaster. Her friend showed her things even Kate hadn't experienced: a transvestite club, new drugs, witchcraft and fortune telling.

"Is there anything this woman hasn't been into?" I didn't hide my disbelief.

"Fortunately, no human being lives long enough to be exposed to the breadth of depravity that exists in this world. There's always more *drama*—as you call it—available: murder, incest, robbery, joy-riding, sadism, torture, kidnapping, blackmail, white-collar crimes, pornography, paedophilia...shall I go on?" Michael's eyes widened as he lowered his chin and gave me a stern look.

"Uh, no. I get the point." I nodded.

"Beware your own fascination with evil."

I felt justly rebuked.

"OK. We are nearly up to date with Kate's story. When she returned to London she decided to go to university. Like so many decisions she had made to start over, this decision, too, ended with her in a worse position than she was previously. She took classes in psychology and philosophy but all she heard was depressing. She was looking for answers but was told there is no purpose to human existence—it's simply a matter of chance that the human race exists at all. She began thinking about life for the first time in years but all she encountered was empty philosophies and increasing personal despair."

"Michael, she seems to have been reaching out for goodness and truth, trying to reform. How could things keep going wrong?"

"This is a sinful and fallen world and she is part of it. This is the mystery of evil. However, she bears fault as well. Every time Teshua sought to help, his help was rejected. It is hard to stay open to goodness and be closed to the grace and mercy offered by the Most High, but this has been her choice."

I was surprised at my own sense of desperation.

Michael continued. "Loneliness was the next step downward. Instead of reaching out to others she turned inward and became despondent and hopeless, unmotivated even to talk. Through her philosophy class she identified herself as 'a prisoner to nihilism'. She has now given up on education as well as faith, success, fame, money, and good looks. She has been tempted by servants of evil and has not said no to them."

"Michael, you said earlier, 'the drama is the same for all human beings.' I just can't see how that is true. My goodness, just look at what has happened to this girl already. My life is tame in comparison."

Michael faced me again. "You can drop the drugs, the promiscuity, the occult from Kate's life. Make her life as boring as you possibly could and you would still be left with the one true drama, the battle for her soul. All the rest is incidental to us. We have seen it all, wild and tame. There is nothing new about it. It is the outcome that matters, not whether it is a colourful story. Everyone we work with is a drama, but it is reality-drama, not theatre, not acting." He paused, but I didn't interrupt.

"Do you know the Lloyd's Bank in Victoria Street?"

I nodded.

"That's where Fiona works. On Thursday, when you saw them happen upon each other, it wasn't pure coincidence. Fiona's guardian angel prompted her to have lunch at a small restaurant in Victoria Station. He knew via Teshua that Kate would be coming that way. With some help, they bumped into each other."

"And conveniently sit at the table next to mine. Was that your doing?"

"No. Coincidences do happen. I would have told you what you overheard had you not gone there for your coffee…Now, how well did Fiona do?"

"Well, she was pretty despondent afterward. I don't think she got through to Kate."

"No she didn't. That is not under her control, but she did what the Most High expected of her, even though she felt confused and ineffective."

"So does that mean Kate has made a turn around?"

"I wish I could say yes. In fact the decision Kate made based on that meeting was not good. This morning Kate went to the chemist's to get a refill on a drug she has been prescribed. She handed the pharmacist her prescription for Tuinal and waited as they filled it." Michael narrated what happened.

'Having trouble sleeping?' The pharmacist asked.

'That's what they're for aren't they.' It wasn't a question. She knew her drugs.

'Take one of these at night just before you go to bed. You shouldn't have any trouble sleeping using these. Make sure you don't exceed your prescription, and under no circumstances should you have any alcohol for at least three hours before taking one.'

The pharmacist gave her the package, and she paid for it on the way out the door.

'Thirty tablets. One month's worth,' she said, 'They will last me a lot longer than that.'

"She then went back to her flat, and that is the situation now. It is time for us to join them."

"Them?"

"You will see, soon. I will take you there."

"Where?"

"To Kate's flat."

As I began to stand, he briefly put his hand on my shoulder and said, "Remain seated. We aren't walking. I will take you there but not by any conventional means. Sit comfortably."

I did. Then Michael lifted his right hand and brought it toward my head. Just as it was about to touch me the room seemed to fill with brilliant light. It was so bright that I couldn't see anything else. Surprisingly, my eyes didn't hurt. The bright light was followed by a very unusual sense of motion. It was smooth, not horizontal but not vertical either, and very swift. In what seemed less than 10 seconds, the sense of motion stopped and the light faded.

My eyes adjusted slowly to the lack of light in the room. As they did, I began to see where we were. As Michael had promised, it was Kate's flat. She, and we, were not alone.

Michael had warned me that I would soon see things I wouldn't normally be able to see, and that Kate, at least, would not be able to see us.

What I saw looked at first like shadows in the air. Gradually, I noticed that these shadows, unlike normal ones, had three dimensions and varying shades of darkness. I could see the contours of what appeared like distorted human faces. I wanted to look away in revulsion yet I didn't. It must have been due to the human fascination with the grotesque. Next I noticed that the air in the room was oppressively thick. It felt greasy or oily. My breathing was laboured, like one experiences when there is an exceptionally low level of oxygen in the air. The temperature was normal, or possibly a little cool, but there was an odour. I can't describe it other than as painful, like smelling a skunk or a badly rotted egg. I wanted to inhale deeply due to the lack of oxygen, but each time I did, I quickly stopped because it hurt.

One of the shadows, the apparent leader, suddenly looked in our direction. I lost my breath, shuddered, and felt my temperature drop. The air wasn't any colder, I was. He must have just noticed our presence. Yet when he looked at us, he didn't seem so much to be looking with his eyes. He was feeling, sensing, assessing. I turned to Michael. Quietly, he answered the question he knew I had.

"Yes, they know we are here. This one is her adversary, the opposite to her guardian angel. His name is Malor. Though he is sensing our presence, you needn't worry, his assessment is that we are not here to interfere and that we have little authority in this situation."

"Why does he think that?"

"Because it is correct. I am here only as an observer. I have been told not to interfere. I am only to explain to you what is happening and why. He senses that to be the case because in this state I reveal only the powers I actually have for this situation. I am no threat to him, so he won't even bother to discover my identity. To him, you appear as my pupil."

I looked around the room. It was a one room flat. It had a small table with two unmatched wooden chairs. Along one wall was a bed. At its head was a lamp-stand with a small lamp. Across the room was an overstuffed chair next to a wardrobe. The third wall had the only window with a shade pulled and curtains drawn. We were standing across from it near the door. There was nothing on the walls except the paint and even that was missing in places. Kate was slouched in the overstuffed chair, her arms hanging over the edge, her head downcast.

As my eyes adjusted further I could see other living shadows. Each was different from the others though they all had a similar terrible coldness in common. Apart from Malor, there seemed to be one of significantly higher rank. His darkness was greater. The air around him appeared more suffocating. He stood across the room in the corner but appeared detached and removed, as though he were simply waiting, for what I do not know.

In a hushed tone, Michael spoke to me. "Do you remember the name Chorbah?"

"From the fall of Satan? Yes. Wasn't he a spirit of despair?"

"Yes, he is here. Malor has called upon him in recent months to finish the work he started. Kate's emptiness has turned into desolation and despair. It is Chorbah's work. He has led Kate to a decision. Tonight she intends to commit suicide. We cannot forcibly stop her as much as we would wish to. Through the years we have brought her much grace from the Most High, but she has too often refused it. Pray that she doesn't tonight."

"But where is the grace to come from? All I see here are the servants of hell. Are there no angels to help? Is she that far gone?"

"Nearly. Only Teshua and Thurian are left. One may speak and one may fight, but there is little left that can reawaken her soul. I expect little will be said, and that may be a while yet. When the time comes that word will have to be brief and piercing. It will be her last chance to respond to the truth before being lost forever in misery, darkness and death."

While he said this, he looked at the small lamp on the nightstand at the head of the bed. It was only then that I saw them. I had been looking for human figures, but these were two small lights, one white and one silver. They were near the lamp but separate from it. Both were dim.

"Teshua and Thurian?" I asked.

"Yes. Their light is weak because she refuses it. In fact their power is greater than either Malor or Chorbah. Teshua, which you see as the white light, has been her guardian and her helper since her birth. He has never taken his eye off her for a moment. Thurian is here on a special assignment. He is a warrior, but he doesn't know yet whether he will be called upon to fight. If he must fight, he will. If not, he will leave. Then hope will vanish quickly and forever."

"How will he know if he must fight?"

"He will know. Watch him closely. If he does not fight tonight, her soul will be lost. Yet, he will only fight when he is called upon in the name of the Most High."

Michael suddenly quit his narration and pointed in the direction of Kate. The demon of despair, Chorbah, was now speaking to her.

"You have finished everything, no more excuses. You are numb to it all. You must escape the emptiness. Your life is empty. You have known it for a long time now. You've proven it over and over. There is only one escape."

"Michael?" I whispered asking for more help to understand.

"Chorbah is one of the most effective. I almost always find him at work where people are contemplating suicide. He does more than just speak of emptiness and despair. He infuses it. He works on people's emotions and attitudes. They feel his work more than they hear it in the mind. Even yesterday Kate would have resisted more. Her reserves are remarkably low. It isn't even a question of the will to live. Her will has been virtually destroyed. She doesn't even think thoughts like, 'I don't care anymore.' She has lost touch with her own thought and feelings.

"When humans say, 'I don't care,' it means that they are still enough in touch to know that they could care, they just don't. In her case she no longer feels caring or not caring at all. She is numb to it. That is when there is real danger of them taking their own life. She has reached the bottom." Michael paused. I heard a woman's voice.

"Everyone is gone. The cleaning ladies have left for the long weekend. Everyone is gone. I have made sure that no one knows that I am here." I realised it must be Kate's voice but I didn't see her lips move at all. Again I looked at Michael.

"You will be allowed to hear some of what she is thinking—though not all. That would be too confusing. You will hear only what she is most conscious of thinking. Of course there is much more going on in her than what you will hear: some of it is barely conscious, some subconscious. There are also motivational and emotional realities, which I can perceive and understand but you will not. It is this ability which makes me able to know exactly what she is feeling and the motivation behind her actions."

"How do you sense that?"

"It is a sense, like seeing and hearing, and is quite reliable. All angels have it, but in differing degrees. It is a very complex faculty. It has to be in order to make sense of the very complex emotions and motivations of human beings. It is a bit like listening to five people speaking to you at one time on how they learned to ride a bicycle and being able to synthesise them into one united report."

"I can't even listen to two people at once."

"It is a sense faculty we angels have but you do not, but it is not difficult for us, any more than hearing, smelling and seeing at the same time are difficult for you."

Michael then continued with his explanation of Kate's condition. "In the last month she has sunk deeper into depression. More and more frequently self-pity, loneliness, fear and despair have paralysed her—not physically, but internally—in her will and her emotions. Her relationship with her family has completely broken down. She cut all communication with her father, and even though she has desperately wanted to speak to her mother, she can't bear to let her come close. She now wants nothing more than to get out—but there has seemed to be no escape. Gradually, and then more frequently, Malor and Chorbah have proposed suicide to her. Each time Teshua has strongly urged her to resist, but lately she has blocked out his voice. The thought of escape now blocks out almost any other thought. She has been given the plan for her suicide. To her, this alone seems to make sense.

"This time she is serious. The first couple of times she considered taking an overdose she backed out. She'd think of her mother, or Fiona, or others. She also held back a couple of times because of small things like overdue books. Now, none of these reservations remain. Escape is all she thinks about."

Suddenly, the phone rang. Malor swore. Kate swore. "Why didn't I unplug that phone?" It was on an end table next to the chair. She didn't want to answer it but she always answered the phone whether she wanted to or not. Her habitual behaviour held. Her hand blindly groped for the phone. On the third ring she found it. Malor came over to Kate's side.

"Hello."

"Kate?" It was her mother.

"Don't answer." It was Malor.

Kate didn't answer. Malor stood near her monitoring the conversation.

"Kate, are you OK?"

Again she didn't answer.

"Fiona said she saw you the other day. She gave me your phone number. Where are you?"

Her mother paused, waited, and then continued.

"She said you had lunch together. How was it?"

Still there was no answer.

"Have you been eating lately? Fiona said that you looked even worse…"

Silence.

"You are eating aren't you?…You are going to waste away…Can I bring you some food?…Where are you living now?"

Malor spoke. "You are leaving today."

"I'm leaving today." Kate mumbled. Malor continued to speak to Kate, and she parroted what he said. She wasn't even hearing what her mother was saying.

"Where?" Her mother asked.

"It's cold and dark here. I'm going to leave."

"When are you going? Kate, where are you going?"

"I don't feel anything anymore. It is all blackness. Inside and out."

"Kate, do you want some help?"

"I don't need any help. You can't help me anymore. I'm not going to see you anymore. Good-bye."

"Kate, you must tell me where you are going?"

"They have come for me, so I am going with them. It is time to go."

"Hang up." Malor commanded.

Kate hung up the phone and unplugged it.

Michael whispered to me. "She didn't even know it was her mother. She just began speaking and quit as she was directed."

Kate moved toward the table and opened a bottle of whisky that was sitting there. Chorbah passed through her mind again and spoke. "Now, no one will interrupt.

No one will prevent. It is all done. Now, take and eat. Take and drink."

Chorbah and Malor looked on, intensely. In the darkest part of the room the third evil presence kept his distance, not moving, speaking or interfering. He simply remained a foreboding presence—an evil waiting its moment.

Kate sat at the table. She took the bottle and filled a glass. She shook five tablets into her hand, threw them into her mouth and swallowed them with the whisky.

In that moment the situation changed. This was no longer some clinical observation for me but a deadly reality. I was seeing Kate taking her own life. I grabbed Michael by the arm. "Don't let her do this. She is going to take her own life! Can't you stop her?"

Michael stopped me with his hand. He was listening. Slowly, a look of sadness came over his face. "No," he sighed, "I cannot."

"But surely you have the power to defeat these demons. Do something!"

"For me it is forbidden."

"Then I'll do something." I tried to move but found I couldn't.

"How clearly you are a son of Adam. Your first thought is to take matters into you own hands, all in the name of salvation of course, but in the process you would cross purposes with the Most High. Your nature is to act rather than to obey. My nature is simply to obey. The thought of acting on my own is not there, the desire to help, yes, but only as commanded."

Chorbah, the Spirit of Despair, spoke again. "Nothingness is your freedom—the final and true escape from all your oppression. You must escape."

Kate took an even larger handful of pills and poured more whisky. In a matter of minutes she had already consumed one half of the bottle. She noticed her motor control was slipping fast.

"Now you must take the rest. One last act of defiance toward this miserable world." This time it was Malor who spoke.

Kate laid out the rest of the pills. "A dozen to go…" In three groups of four she swallowed them, each with a small amount of whisky. Then she started to drink the rest of the whisky.

"Two glasses to go." She thought.

"Do it quickly." Malor was provoking her. "Down it."

She took two large swallows and got them down. Her throat was numb, but her lungs were still alive. The whisky burned. Her lungs revolted. She coughed a mouthful back out, some of it going through her nose.

"Fool!" Said Malor to her. Then he turned to Chorbah. "Utterly despicable. What, in all that is, is lower than the human being? Not just fools, but proud fools every one of them. She is clay in my hands, but lower than the dirt from which she is made."

Chorbah responded to Malor's claim. "Clay in your hands! Your hands, Ha! I am here because you can't complete the work. Why is that? Softness? Stupidity? Incompetence? Who has brought her to the point of desolation? She is empty, void of love, void of goodness. Who has brought her to the point of despair? ME!" he said, pointing to his chest. "Soon she will enter my emptiness, not yours. It is my spiritual void calling, one she will never escape. Never! She shall become the emptiness she hates. She will embrace what she seeks to escape,…and once in my embrace, she will never escape again."

Chorbah spoke to Kate now. "Welcome your despair, my dear. I will be your master. Chorbah has come. Welcome him just as he welcomes you! Yes, through me you will escape the bondage of life through the freedom of death."

"And only to run into the arms of a bondage much worse." He added, speaking to Malor. "This bondage will be total and eternal. You have tasted but a portion of despair. You have only licked true emptiness."

"As a dog returns to its vomit…" It was Malor now. "I will make her end yet more degraded…"

"No!" Chorbah raised his hand to silence Malor. "Be cautious. Even small things can bring them to back out. Pain or even shame."

"Shut up! I know what I am doing. I have known her since birth. She is putty in my hands. There is more evil to be done here. Why stop short!"

"I have seen our enemies use anything to fulfil their purposes. Malor, your boldness is the trait of a fool."

"Do you presume to call me a fool? You? You are good for one thing alone, a specialist who knows everything about nothing. I know this rotten race. I have studied them. You only come and go as you are called. I'm the one who has done all the work, day in and day out. For you it is a privilege to work with me! Just remember who is in charge here!" Malor continued to mock Choreb.

Kate poured the last glass and stumbled over to her bed next to the wall. The glass somehow made it to the nightstand, and she fell onto her back on the bed. Her eyes began to glaze as she stared at the ceiling.

Malor spit at Choreb. "Your work is done. The time has come."

Now the darkest of the shadows, the one that had spent most of the time silently waiting in the corner, came forward and approached the bed. No change registered in the two points of light near the lamp as the darkness approached. The shadow was tall, over eight feet, very dark and very cold. As it reached the bed, it raised its arms from its sides and reached into its chest. It withdrew a sword as black as itself. "Terror" was the name written in red on the side of the sword facing me.

"Death." Michael whispered. "Malor has called him."

"Is death in Malor's domain? Can he determine it?" I blurted out.

Michael's hand came quickly to my mouth to quieten me. "Determine it? No. But he does know the laws that govern life. Kate has broken them. Her body is not capable of handling the mixture of drugs and alcohol. This particular combination will strike fast when it reaches her central nervous system. Malor can see that as clearly as I. It is only a matter of minutes in the quantity she took.

"Almost everything now hangs in the balance for Kate. Her final choice is upon her. Unless I am mistaken Malor will permit Death to manifest himself to her so that he might take her life at the moment of starkest fear. You will see it in her eyes."

Death looked from the bedside back toward Malor, who nodded his head. With that, death took his sword in both hands, set the point of the sword on her bed and leaned the shaft and hilt in front of her face. Now he turned completely dark. No light passed through him at all. He passed his left hand through Kate's eyes.

Suddenly, her eyes grew wide with horror. She saw him and realised in an instant, with terrible clarity that she was going to die, and she didn't know what was going to happen next. A deep, long howl came from her mouth. The countenance of Death was unchanged. He absorbed her terror but found no delight in it. Kate called for help. Her cry was met with silence. Again she cried out, but no one heard. In desperation she banged against the pipes on the wall, but no one was even there to hear.

"Kate, my dear," in an artificially sweet voice Malor spoke, "you have planned this well. There is no one around. You wanted no chance of rescue, and now, there is none. Welcome your escape. You have come to the arms of Death."

Thurian, the silver light began to fade. It moved from the lamp, passed through the wall on the opposite side of the bed and left the room.

I could not watch. I closed my eyes and turned my head. "Oh, God…" But Michael took me by the arm and said, "You must watch."

As I did, Death raised his sword in both hands above her head and held it there. He waited as her fear multiplied and then multiplied again. Terror and Death had come to take her. Her fear now left her paralysed. She could no longer move her body. Death slowly began straightening to his full height, extending his arms above his head, the point of his sword two feet above her fear filled eyes.

He reached his full extension. As he did, quickly, urgently and quietly, a new voice spoke. It came from near the lamp on the stand. "Call out for help. Now! You know your only hope." It was the voice of Teshua.

Kate drew in a last gasp of air, held it and cried, "Noooo! Help! Help me!" Neither Teshua nor Thurian moved. "Help me! She cried out again into the void. The sword of Death came crashing down toward Kate's body just as she exhaled crying, "Jesus, help!"

The great burst of silver light that followed should have blinded me but somehow didn't. It came right through the wall above her bed and lighting up the whole room in a flash. From within the brightness a beam of silver light arced across to the sword of Death just as it impacted Kate's body. The impact of the light against the sword created a sound, which shook the entire flat as "Terror" splintered into a thousand shards of darkness. Thurian had been commanded to fight.

Chorbah instantly perceived what had happened and roared with anger. He turned toward Malor and cried "Fooooool!" Yet Malor was the first to act. In one deep breath he inhaled the dark shadow that was Chorbah. Malor condensed into even greater blackness. Instantly there was the sound of rushing wind as Malor exhaled the blackness of Chorbah directly at Kate in an attempt to destroy Thurian's momentary flash of hope with the full weight of despair.

Thurian, the silver bolt of light, which had splintered "Terror", saw what was happening to Chorbah through Malor and instantly changed form into that of a silver shield and dropped over Kate. He and Chorbah arrived instantaneously. Again there was a burst of light, a shattering of darkness, a crash as of steel on steel, followed by a long loud groan of anger and agony: "DAMN YOU!" was the cry of the demon, Chorbah, as he disappeared.

Meanwhile, more and more small and flickering lights entered the room: pink, blue, silver, gold, green…Most of them were surrounding Kate on her bed; many of them were passing through her. It was impossible to tell if she was still conscious but she had a look of peace that replaced the look of terror, which had been there a moment before.

Death had stepped aside as soon as "Terror" splintered. He had continued to watch dispassionately, his face blank, empty, expressionless. Now, he slowly turned and began to walk back toward his corner. As he reached the wall he turned, deliberately, and for the first time, spoke. "Only for now," he said in a voice deeper and darker than any I have ever heard, "she, and all, are mine,…in time." With that, he passed through the wall and disappeared.

Suddenly the atmosphere of the room changed. A radiating warmth, like sunshine, replaced the coolness. It seemed to come from flickering lights surrounding and passing through Kate. The air cleared and became unusually pleasant to breathe, more invigorating than clear mountain air.

I looked around the room. Only Malor was left, hardly visible in the brightness of the room. By now there were hundreds of small independent lights passing in through the walls toward and then through

Malor's shadow. Slowly he lost shape. His darkness dispersed and from what I could tell nearly disappeared.

I looked again at Kate. "What is happening to her?" I asked. "I thought you said she would die from the overdose?"

"No," corrected Michael, "I said, 'It is only a matter of minutes in the quantity she took.' Life and death ultimately lie in the hands of the Most High alone. In his mercy, he has chosen not to allow her to die at this time. You are witnessing a miracle, a temporary suspension of the laws of nature."

"Will they heal her then?" I asked.

"Most definitely not. They will only sustain her in life. She will not awake again for a full 24 hours. The combination of drugs and alcohol would have easily killed her. She needs to know and remember that for the rest of her life."

"It is a good thing she didn't wait one second more."

"It is a good thing he didn't wait one second more."

"Thurian?"

"No. Malor. Had Kate lost consciousness before seeing death I believe she would have never cried for help. Malor made a big mistake."

That was the last I remember of Kate's room. In the next moment, I found myself kneeling in the chapel. My eyes were adjusting to what seemed to be very dim lighting, even though it was the normal lighting in the cathedral. When I looked around, Michael was not there.

I was stunned. I didn't remember kneeling down; I wasn't sure what had just happened. Whatever it was, was more intense than any film or dream I could remember. My heart was pounding. The images of Malor, Chorbah and Death raced before my mind's eye, and for a moment a chill went through my body. It was quickly replaced by the fleeting image of Kate, lying on the bed, surround by the flickering lights. More images passed through my mind, nearly as vivid and clear as they had been just moments previous and I found myself thanking God for what had happened.

The hand on my shoulder suddenly me brought back to the reality of the moment. The hand belonged to a warden. "I am sorry to interrupt your prayer, but the cathedral is closing for the night."

"Sorry," I said as I looked at my watch. Over an hour had passed since the end of the service.

"Nothing to be sorry about. I did not want to disturb you until I had to. You seemed lost in better world."

"Did I disturb anyone?" I asked, not knowing exactly what I had been doing during my "prayer."

"No, I don't think so." He said, but I couldn't tell if he was just being polite.

I rose and left the cathedral. As I returned to my hotel, I wondered when I would next see Michael.

CHAPTER 7:

THE RESURRECTION

It seemed odd to me at first, a memo from an angel, but if there was one thing about Michael that I knew, it was that I never knew what he would do next. On Holy Saturday I went down to the hotel restaurant for breakfast. When I returned to my room, a memo lay on my bed. I do not know how it got there. I rang the front desk but the hotel had not delivered it. It was typed and had no signature. (Not that a signature would prove much. I just wouldn't mind having an angel's autograph.) It read as follows:

"Meet me at 10:30 p.m. tonight, at Westminster cathedral, for the Easter Vigil. Michael."

I spent the day doing travel agency work at my computer. I knew I would be unable to complete my work, but I wanted to note a few more thoughts before they escaped me. I decided to take my miniature tape recorder with me on the underground and record them. I could write up what I had recorded later. It was a bit awkward to make a tape while on the underground but it was easier than trying to write. In the end, the whirring, grinding, electric and metal sounds that are part of a ride on the Underground, made the tape almost inaudible but I somehow managed. It was only as I finished my agency work that it struck me. "Why hadn't I been recording my conversations with

Michael?" He was visible to others. He must also be audible! Now was my chance.

I left the station and walked down Victoria Street, toward the cathedral at 10:15 p.m. There are fewer trains late at night, but my connections had been good. I would arrive easily before 10:30. It had been raining heavily all day and had stopped just before I left the hotel. The air was still heavy with mist and it formed golden halos around the amber streetlights. The rain made for an unusually quiet Saturday night in the city. Many people chose to stay at home.

"You are early!"

I stopped, turned and saw Michael walking up from behind. I clandestinely turned on my tape recorder, leaving it in the pocket of my coat. Just as I did, a taxi screeched to a halt, barely avoiding a pedestrian. I turned toward the street and looked, but everyone was safe.

The taxi-driver angrily sounded his horn at the pedestrian, and continued on his way.

Michael joined me and asked, "Is it working?" nodding toward my tape recorder.

"I was going to ask you if would mind."

"I don't mind at all. Is it working? Check it."

I removed the tape recorder from my pocket. The batteries were dead.

"Unfortunately, you will not find a place to purchase batteries at 10:15 p.m."

"Would I have been able to record your voice?" I asked.

"Yes."

I was as disappointed to hear that, as I would have been to hear 'No.'

Michael began walking with me toward the cathedral. I asked him another question.

"Michael, what happened when you took me to Kate's room? Was I really there?"

"Yes and no. It has to do with the interaction of energy, matter and time…"

"Wait! I don't think I asked the question I wanted to ask. I wasn't looking for a scientific explanation. What I really want to know is what has happened to her?"

"It's a good sign that you are more concerned for her than understanding what happened. She is doing well. Here is what happened after we left.

Teshua stood guard as Kate slept, never leaving her side, never distracted. The dull assignment was not resented. Having fought for her for twenty-two years, the break-through was a source of rejoicing. The sheep that was lost now had been found. Yet Teshua knew that the battle for her was not yet ended. Malor had not given up even though he and his allies had suffered a major setback. They had successfully turned many experiences of this type to their own ends, often within the first few hours or days. They were plotting the quick uprooting of this seed of life.

Twenty-four hours after slipping into safe oblivion, Kate stirred. Her clothes were soaked in perspiration from her body's fight to purge itself of the drugs and alcohol. She inhaled deeply and brought her hands to her face, brushing away her hair. Her hands flopped back onto the bed; she had yet to open her eyes.

Teshua saw her stir and immediately doubled his guard. He expected to see Malor return. He was not surprised as a shadow began to appear near Kate. Teshua had been given instructions on how to handle this. He suspected he knew what Malor would do, assuming he followed the standard pattern.

Malor approached the side of the bed. Teshua moved around to the head. This would be another in their seemingly endless verbal wars.

Teshua passed his hand through Kate's head. 'A memory,' he whispered. 'A memory of peace and joy. The sudden disappearance of despair replaced by an unanticipated hope.'

'Yet it wasn't exactly like that.' Malor now spoke to her. 'It certainly wasn't an experience of him.'

The word 'God' seldom issues from their mouths. It is a painful memory of what they have lost. If they can avoid saying it, or 'Lord' or 'Jesus' they will.

'Truly,' Malor continued, 'you have never had a high like that before. It would be well worth doing it again. A drug experience like that is well worth the risk. You certainly didn't experience him while you were on drugs. That isn't the way religious experiences work. You came to the edge of the abyss of death, the ultimate experience. In death you found life. How much more it would have been true if you had only gone one step further. Total emptiness was the source of your freedom. Come again! Let the numbness return. Don't feel. Don't think. In nothingness you are free from everything. You tasted it. How good and tantalising it was. Come, drink fully of death this time.'

Kate's eyes grew wide. A look of fear passed over her face. Her emptiness was returning. Again Teshua passed his hand through Kate's mind. 'Think! Remember the void. Yes, remember the fear. You saw death. Death! In it was no joy. The good taste you remember is fullness, not emptiness. Do you want fear and death to return? Remember what happened. You planned it all perfectly. It was enough narcotics and whisky to kill you three times over. What saved you? It was not mind over matter. You had done what was necessary to kill yourself. It was something beyond you. There is a source of love, a source of hope. You can know him.'

Teshua's mind lifted to intercession. The room began filling with the presence of hundred's of lights of various shades and hues, again covering Kate's body. Slowly, she swung her legs over the side of the bed and sat up on the edge. 'I think there is hope. But how can I find it.' She did not move. Tears came to her eyes and ran down her cheeks, slowly at first, but then in a flood. After ten minutes, which seemed forever to Kate, the initial, overwhelming grace of longing for hope and truth passed.

'Fiona,' prompted Teshua. 'Fiona is where you have seen it before: this hope, this love.'

Kate rose, went to the phone and began to dial, and then noticed there was no dial tone. She found the phone lead and was about to plug it in, but then hesitated.

'Not now, later.' Malor had returned to his work. 'What will you say? How can you go back to her after what you said? What will she think? Have you suddenly become religious? You know better. You don't want her sympathy. You don't want her pity. What if she starts putting pressure on you again?'

Kate plugged in the phone, saying to herself, She's not likely to be at home on a Saturday night anyway. It was an attempt at self-delusion. She knew she did not want to take a firm decision yet. She dialled Fiona's number, expecting no answer, but willing to talk if she happened to reach her. The phone rang at the other end of the line—once, twice. Kate found herself not knowing what to hope for: an answer, or no answer. It continued to ring a third and fourth time. In the middle of the fifth ring the phone was answered, the sound was mechanical, 'Hi! It's Fiona. I'm sorry. I'm not in...' Now Kate had to decide whether to leave a message.

'Don't bother. Ring her later when you know what you want to say.' Malor was first to respond. Kate assented internally. Just then, the tape stopped and Fiona answered.

'Hello! This is Fiona. Sorry about the tape. I couldn't get the phone quickly enough.'

'Fiona?'

'Yes.'

'It's Kate.'

'Kate?' There was a note of surprise in Fiona's voice. She tried to hide it quickly…'Hi! How are you?'

'OK, I guess. And you?'

'Fine, thanks. Yah. Fine.' Fiona hesitated just a brief moment in case Kate wanted to continue. She was uncertain how to handle the phone call. It was completely out of character for Kate. Fiona decided Kate probably wanted her to take the initiative, but where? How? 'So, ah,…what have you been up to, Kate?'

'Don't tell her! Certainly don't tell her about this so called religious experience!' Malor jumped in.

'Nothing much, mostly staying here in my flat.'

'Sounds a bit lonely. Hey, how about coming to visit sometime?'

Malor jumped in. 'Kate, it's a brush off. Come visit me sometime.'

'Yah. Sometime.' Kate's voice was flat. Fiona caught it. She was afraid Kate might hang up.

'Wait a minute.' Fiona had to come up with an idea, any idea. 'What am I doing tonight?'

She thought, and then asked Kate, 'What are you doing tonight?'

'I hadn't made any plans.' Kate's voice was still flat, expressionless.

'Can you come to church with me?' As soon as she said it, Fiona regretted it. 'Church???' She thought, 'what a mistake.'

'Not church! Not religion!' It was Malor again. 'You hate it. You're not interested. Just say no thanks.'

'You want her hope, her joy. Give her a chance,' said Teshua.

'Kate?...Are you still there?'

'...Church?'

Fiona inhaled quickly, she hadn't lost Kate yet, but how could she get her to think positively about going to church?

'I think you'll like it. We never went to one like this when we were young.'

'I don't know...'

Fiona's mind was racing, 'O, Lord, now what do I say? Should I back off and propose something else? The cinema maybe? She didn't have time to think. 'It would be great to have you come along!' The words were out of her mouth before she could make a good decision. 'I could meet you at the Victoria Clock at 11:45. It starts at midnight. It will go for a couple of hours.' Fiona paused, nervously.

Kate didn't respond immediately, finally she said. 'Midnight? That doesn't sound like a very typical church service.'

'Go for it!' The thought flashed through Fiona's mind. 'Oh, it's not, believe me. I told you it wouldn't be. I can explain more when we get there…Can you come?' She pressed for an answer.

'I suppose so. I guess I could give it a try.'

'Can't hurt. If you don't like it we can do something else.'

'Ok. Oh, what should I wear?'

Fiona smiled, thinking, 'That's the old Kate.' She answered. "Uhm, do you still have that red dress with white trim?"

'I haven't worn that in months, but I think I still have it.'

'You look great in it. Try that one.' (Anything but black, she thought.)

'I'll see if I can find it…what time and where again?"

'The Victoria Clock at 11:45.'

'Ok.'

'Great, I'll meet you then in a couple of hours! Bye!'

'Yah, bye…' Kate's voice was showing signs of life.

Malor retreated again in defeat and began thinking about a new strategy.

"Michael," I asked, "Has or will Malor given up?"

"He will not give up on Kate until she is dead. He will harass her for the rest of her life. Fortunately, his power over her has been greatly reduced in the last twenty-four hours. Still, neither he nor we would ever admit defeat nor claim victory until the very end when she is safely delivered into the hands of the Most High, or when she is lost to Satan forever."

"Won't she see right through the emptiness of his deceit from now on?"

"Often, yes, but he is a master of disguise. My guess is that she, and Teshua, will have to fight long and hard. Malor will seek to colour her memory and twist her dreams. He knows that the road to hell must not be void of pleasure. He will remind her only of the joys of her previous life: the travel, the parties, the nice clothes and the adventure of it all. The pain, the loneliness, the despair and much else that was evil he will try to hide. He will also seek to distort her perception of her new life. Faithfulness will be called dull. Love will be called obligation and bondage. Love for her by other Christians will seem like condescending pity. Holiness will always seem out of her reach. Malor's name means emptiness. He will always seek to isolate her and to draw her back into the empty way of life she had led. To do this he must get her to abandon all truth and love. It will not be easy for him, especially if Kate openly receives the amount of grace that is available to her. In fact, tonight you will see that grace even more clearly. So will she. She needs to grow into giving the full response the Most High seeks from her. It still isn't exactly clear to her what or who she is looking for in going to the church. She was prepared to admit that it might be God, but she still isn't happy about all this 'Jesus' stuff, and she is a bit sceptical about what relevance anything in his life might have for her life."

Michael was leading me toward the front doors of the cathedral. Somehow it seemed more and more like I was visiting him at his home. Some home!

"Time is passing. We must finish the story quickly." Michael said as he walked with a purpose toward the main sanctuary. We finally stopped before a mosaic of the resurrection in the apse on the left.

"I will continue the other story where I left off on Friday." Michael began.

For two days the Roman guards assigned by Pilate watched and waited without incident. They didn't expect one. They dismissed the prediction of a resurrection on the third day. Still, Roman guards were always alert. They were trained to be alert. Day or night, it didn't matter. With or without an expected incident, they watched carefully. All through the night they patrolled back and forth, watching for any sign of activity, but there was none—at least none that they could see.

Two guards were patrolling in front of the tomb. One was a Greek from Antioch, Aristides by name. He had grown up being exposed to the many forms of religion in Antioch—a cosmopolitan city. The second guard, Quintus, was from Rome. Although Rome was also a cosmopolitan city and home to many religious beliefs, his faith was first, last and always in the empire. Everything else was inferior. There was not much to do as watchmen by night. They passed the second night's deepest hours of darkness in conversation. That was all that broke the stillness.

'Well, if the rumours are true, we will find out tonight.' Aristides said it aloud mostly to pass the time, but Quintus gladly responded in order to break the monotony.

'You don't believe in that ridiculous twaddle do you?'

'I said if…' Aristides wondered in a hushed tone. He realised the danger of leaving his statement there. He spoke louder now, 'If it's all hogwash, then of course I won't believe. Fables and fairy tales, who believes in fables and fairy tales—if that's what they are? I just said if…'

'Come on! They have to be. Who has ever known someone to rise from the dead?'

'Who ever knew of anyone conquering the entire world? But Alexander did it, and before the Romans! We were sent here just in case this Jesus does rise from the dead. At least someone thinks there is something to worry about.'

'Forget that argument. We're not here because anyone expects a resurrection. We're here because Pilate just wanted to be rid of those members of the Sanhedrin who were pestering him. He wants to put this whole affair behind him as quickly as possible. Messiahs and resurrections have nothing to do with us being here.'

'But what do you make of that other case?'

'What do you mean?'

'You know what I mean. Lazarus. That was what started this in the first place. Scores of people claimed this Jesus raised him from the dead. His family had buried him in a sealed tomb and four days later, Jesus raised him from the dead, or so they say.'

'So they say...'

'But you can't argue that Lazarus isn't alive.'

'No, but was he really dead?'

'I can't prove it, but then I can't prove that he wasn't. A lot of people have testified that he was.'

'So what, they're Jews.'

'What do you make of what happened in Capernaum?'

'The centurion's servant?'

'Yes.'

'I don't know.'

'The centurion is no Jew. Why would he claim that this Jesus healed his servant?'

'Maybe he owed him something. Blackmail maybe...'

'Come on, no centurion is blackmailed by a self proclaimed itinerant rabbi.'

'So, maybe he healed the man. What does it matter?'

'It means he could be this Messiah everyone is talking about.'

'You mean, could have been. He's dead. You saw him. We sealed the tomb. He's dead. Cold, stiff and dead—Messiah or no Messiah—he's dead.'

'Suppose he rises from the dead like they say he claimed he would, then what?'

'Suppose the sun rises in the west tomorrow. Suppose trees can paint. Suppose horses can whistle. When I see it, I'll believe it, not before.'

'Well, what about the other centurion and his men? You heard what they said when they came back from the scene of the crucifixion. They are convinced that he is the Son of God.'

'So what! What if they came back telling you they were convinced he was Julius Caesar? Would you believe that, too?'

'Hold on, I never said I believed any of this. I am just asking questions. I am interested in the truth here.'

'What is truth?'

'The truth is what matters. Suppose we have only been told we are getting paid for this miserable assignment but it turns out not to be true: What do you think of that? To have it said publicly that your wife is cheating on you, when she isn't: What about that? Truth matters.'

'I suppose…'

'Well, then, suppose he rises from the dead? Think about that.'

'You think about it. I know what is important. It's here in my scabbard. Rome conquered by the sword. That's what's important to understand. If he rises, he will either come with me to Pilate or he will go right back into the tomb with some steel in his stomach.'

'Some good that will do.'

'What do you mean?'

'I mean that if he rose from the dead, what good will killing him do? He'll just rise again.' This time Quintus was slower in his response.

'So what do we do?'

'I don't know.'

'He just better stay dead.'

'Maybe…Quintus, I think I am going to have a talk with this Lazarus.'

Silence returned. The guards continued to patrol, waiting for morning.

Toward the end of the night, the host of heaven were given orders to report to the garden at Golgotha, just outside the walls of Jerusalem. Each of us drew near quietly. We had been told to come, but not to manifest our glory at all. Angels of all ranks and orders were there, waiting, silent. From time to time, others would arrive, messengers sent without a message, warriors sent without battle instructions, comforters sent with no one to comfort. We were all to wait, silently.

The night was heavily overcast, the clouds still unbroken. The darkness was yet undisturbed. As it drew closer to the dawn, the angels of worship began to appear. The throne room in heaven was shrouded now in stillness, empty save for the presence of the Most High.

We were not the only ones to arrive in force. The powers of darkness were present as well. They too had heard the claim of Jesus, only they didn't believe it. Our enemy is no fool. The threat had to be responded to in some way, so he sent his minions to do battle if it were necessary on the morning of the third day. As yet they didn't know whether it would be necessary. They too waited silently.

I looked at the heavens, knowing the time was drawing near. The clouds were breaking, blowing across a sky illuminated only by the stars. The just-past-full moon had already set. Still, we waited.

In the land of shadows, the dim and silent world where light does not penetrate, the souls of the dead were waiting—never thinking, never acting, never changing,—but waiting in the quiet and empty darkness. All who were sons and daughters of Adam and Eve— Abraham and Moses, Ruth and Esther—the known and the unknown still existed but mute and motionless, unaware of time, without sensation or thought.

Into this pale, faint world the human soul of the Son of Man descended, fulfilling all righteousness, entering the deathly destiny of his race, another soul added to the countless number held imprisoned by Shakhath, the angel of the abyss. Like all the other souls, this soul came to its place of rest and was still. Shakhath had been warned in advance. He was to watch

163

this soul carefully. Might this usher in the first of the fateful days, rumoured from of old, the Day of the Righteous One? A day only less feared than the rumoured Day of Destruction when Hades was to be cast into Gehennna, the everlasting fire. But these were rumours, only rumours, passed quietly through the Horde of Hell and denounced by their master. Still, the rumours kept returning. They seemed to have a life of their own. Thirty some years ago they had come to life again, then died, and now they had reappeared.

Like all the horde, Shakhath knew better than to believe in a rumour and he knew better than to oppose his master or to question his master's judgement publicly. However, he also knew better than to believe the Master of Hell, the Father of Lies. For now he would follow his orders—orders given to him in secret thousands of years ago 'in the very, very unlikely case' that there were such a day as conveyed in the rumours.

His orders, should the Righteous One arise or in any way seek to open the gates of Hades, were to summon the Horde of Hell to war. The gates of Hades had to be held lest the powers of death be damaged or destroyed. He waited and watched the most recently arrived soul, the soul of this son of Nazareth.

Shakhath had been warned to be alert again, just as he had been warned at the death of Moses, at the death of David, at the death of Isaiah, at the death of others. Nothing had happened then. Nothing would happen now. The souls of the dead had no power. This job had been monotonous from the very beginning. Even the deaths of the 'potential Messiahs' had become one tedious experience after another. 'This is monotony spiced only with boredom.' Shakhath said to his millions of souls who did not hear.

The hours began to pass as normal. The quietness of death was undisturbed. Shakhath relaxed. 'Nothing had changed and nothing will.' He thought.

Suddenly, silently, a ray of energy emanated from the Son of Man. It was undetectable to all but the first born soul, toward whom it was directed. Adam was awakened. Another ray issued forth. The soul of Abel, the first-born unto death, imprisoned in darkness since the very beginning of the era of man, assimilated the energy of life.

The number of invisible rays suddenly increased, multiplying in every direction. Still, the pall over Hades remained. Not a soul had moved, not a sound was heard.

Then the voice of Job broke forth, loud and with piercing clarity: 'I know my redeemer lives and in my flesh I shall see God.' His voice was followed immediately by that of David, 'God will ransom my soul from the power of Sheol, for he will receive me'. Then Asaph cried out, 'You guide me with your counsel, and afterward you will receive me to glory.' The words of life spoken centuries before were finding their fulfilment. The souls of the just were wakening.

Finally, the word was spoken to all in Hades who had yet remained untouched: 'Awake, oh sleeper! Arise from the dead, and I shall give you light. Death and darkness are vanquished. I come to set the captives free and lead them to glory. Grace and mercy accompany me, faith will follow me, paradise opens before me.' The souls of the dead responded. All hell was breaking loose.

Shakhath's boredom was over in an instant. The shock lasted but seconds. He quickly gave the call to action.

It was then that I noticed a small break in the clouds. The sky behind it began to show the most faint light. The sun was working its way toward us from below the eastern horizon.

Immediately, there came from above, a long, single ray of lightning, splitting the clouds and piercing the rock where the tomb had been hewn. The ground underfoot rumbled and quaked, knocking the Roman guards from their feet.

At that moment Shakhath countered what was happening with a cry, 'Defend the gates!' But it was too late. Light shattered the darkness of Hades, light from above and light from within, a bright, brilliant, blinding light bearing the burden of the weight of the glory of the Most High. Night outshone the day in an instant. Bonds were broken. Shackles were shattered. Chains were charred and fetters fell away as the Gates of Death were blasted open. The earth had groaned as Jesus died. Now Hades was groaning as Jesus rose.

At that moment the Horde of Hell knew it had not been summoned without purpose. All of them began to rush toward us. The battle was begun.

Every angel now became brilliant, reflecting the glory of the Most High, but something new was reflected: the unique, unforeseen and unimaginable glory of the risen Son of Man. The demonic horde wretched in horror. The clarion cry of conquest combined with the glory and greatness of grace were difficult for them to manage. They despised the light and the glory of heaven even more than the empty darkness of hell. Light was piercing the darkness and the darkness could not overcome it. In every case, the glory of true loyalty revealed the depravity of their allegiance to the Master of Hell. Every demon was again, unavoidably aware of his disastrous choice to follow Satan. The extent of their empty, wasted existence pained them as it was exposed to the extensive excellence of light. Again they felt the weight of glory and still they refused to yield.

An angel of unselfish love manifested its truth and glory to a demon of self-centredness. The demon experienced his emptiness again in the presence of his adversary's fullness and glory. Still, he persisted in his choice against what is beautiful and good, and then fled, wounded by the truth.

An angel of hope manifested itself to an angel of despair. Yet again due to the satanic art of deception, the freedom of hope appeared to be a painful form of depravity. The angel of despair fled into the night, aware of his slavery and unwilling to be set free. One angelic confrontation after another brought the same result. Dismay died before delight. Greed gave way to generosity and cruelty collapsed before kindness. Doubt was driven out by devotion, lust by love, cowardice by courage, and fear by faith.

Now, another light, again an angel, came from above. The stone sealing the sepulchre was being rolled away. As a crack between the stone and the sepulchre swelled, another light issued forth. Suddenly, the whole area was ablaze with radiant splendour. Each of us grew yet again in reflected glory and power. The tomb was opened and the Lord of Life emerged. Jesus victorious, vanquishing sin. Jesus triumphant, destroying death. Christ conquering, having passed through the gates of Hades and setting the host of captives free...

The resurrection of the Son of Man dismayed the Sons of Hell. They considered the Incarnation a disgrace, but this was worse. For them the Son of God should have never become a man, something lower than the angels themselves. Now their worst fear had come true: a son of man was exalted above the glory of the angels. In the resurrected Christ they knew that the love, glory and power of the Most High would forever shine in the face of a man, opening the way for the glorification of every man, woman and child born to the sons of Adam and the daughters of Eve. A wail of indescribable, hate-filled agony went up from the horde as they fled, every one of them, searching for a place of darkness to wallow in their despair.

A shout went up from the angelic host as those bound by sin and death were set free by their great deliverer. This was the hour of glory, the initial fulfilment of the plan of the Most High for the restoration of the fallen planet and its fallen race. This was the pinnacle of human history.

How could we help but sing songs of exultation and rejoice with exceedingly great joy. Salvation had come, death was damned, sin was vanquished, Hades was plundered and Satan was crippled. The human race was now redeemed and the gates of heaven were opened!

Every angel has been given a voice with which to worship the Most High. This was a song of victory and triumph unlike any ever heard before or since. It will ring through the ages, until one day...but more on that later.

Once again, this all happened in a moment of time. It was over as soon as it had begun in the realm of time and space, except for the guards.

Aristides and Quintus were shocked. They had fallen to the ground at the earthquake. Then as the stone was rolled away, they were blinded by the light. When they had recovered their sight, all was quiet but for the pounding of their hearts.

'What was that?' Asked Quintus, lying on his stomach looking toward the tomb.

'I don't know.' Fear had gripped both of them, but they conquered it quickly. They had been trained in the Roman army. They both stood.

'Draw your sword.' Aristides didn't need to say it. Quintus had drawn it as soon as he had regained his feet. Swords drawn, they approached the tomb. Their hearts were racing. They knew they must look. They approached from either side of the mouth of the tomb, their backs to the outside walls. The moment had come. They looked at each other across the mouth of the tomb. Quintus nodded and, simultaneously, they both charged into the entrance, ready for what might come, but not ready for what they saw. They froze.

'Nothing!'

'It's empty…'

'Where did he go?'

'What in the name of Caesar happened! I don't understand this.'

Quintus looked at Aristides and then looked again into the tomb.

'Now what?' Asked Aristides, still looking into the empty tomb, not expecting an answer.

Quintus paused, then responded. 'We must report. We must go to Pilate and tell him.'

'That wasn't what I was asking, Quintus. What about those fables? What about these claims that he would rise from the dead? Now what? What do you think? What do you do?'

"What did they do?" I asked.

"They acted as you might expect. Quintus was paid to keep quiet and he did. He never spoke about what he saw. 'Nothing happened,' he would say. He even came to believe that was the case. He talked himself into it. Aristides, on the other hand, did a lot of thinking about the Jewish 'fables', spoke to Lazarus and eventually became a disciple."

"Michael, it surprises me that a witness to the resurrection itself could just deny it happened so easily."

"Yes, but it is no different now. People disbelieve because they do not want to believe, not because they lack evidence. They just aren't scientific enough in their thinking about it."

"Not scientific enough?"

"True science unveils reality, facts. Argument ceases when truth confronts. People fear the truth. Options close. Choice ceases. Two plus two equals four, case closed. Facing *spiritual* truth is the same, and it will always lead you back to the *fundamental* choice—a choice many people do not want to make, but in so doing, they have made their choice."

171

CHAPTER 8:

THE VIGIL CONTINUES

Michael led me back to the entrance of the cathedral. It was 11:45pm on Holy Saturday. As we reached the beginning of the long nave, a man dressed in a red robe with black trim handed each of us a candle and pointed forward. Michael nodded and we walked up the centre aisle taking seats half way up. We had a good view all the way to the front. The cathedral was already getting full although the vigil was only scheduled to start at midnight. All were waiting in subdued anticipation. Some were silent. Some whispered quietly to others nearby.

Michael, sitting beside me, leaned over putting his hand on my shoulder, and spoke quietly.

"Tonight your eyes will be spiritually opened, as will your ears. Do not be surprised by what you see and hear. It will be a clearer picture of reality than you have ever seen before."

He finished his comment and removed his hand. As he did, I began to perceive something in front of me. As the shape gradually became clear I realised it must be an angel. In colour it was light blue, but it was hard to say whether it was a light or a cloud. When I focused my eyes on the angel it seemed to become more and more solid, but as soon as I shifted my focus and looked at the people in the pew, I could see right through the angel as if it wasn't even there.

I began to focus on the angel in front of me again. As I did others also gradually became visible and within a few minutes I realised that the entire cathedral was filled with them. The angels were dressed in robes, and each emitted a dim light. Some were blue, others silver, gold, red...Each was standing straight and still. They too awaited the beginning of the vigil service.

At 11:55 I looked at my watch and then turned to the back of the cathedral. Fiona and Kate had just arrived. They were handed candles. Kate had a look of great curiosity on her face. She also seemed completely out of place. She certainly was wearing more rings than anyone else in the crowd and her particular red dress and her makeup weren't exactly commonplace. Fiona took her by the arm and led her up the aisle. As it turned out, they ended up one row diagonally in front of us.

Behind Kate I saw Teshua, alert, attentive. Kate turned to Fiona. "Why are there so few lights on in here? Why the silence? What is going on? Is this a special service?"

Although she clearly was whispering, I could hear her. Michael's words came back to mind. "Tonight your eyes will be opened further, as will your ears. Do not be surprised by what you see and hear."

Before Fiona could answer, the congregation began to rise, starting at the front of the cathedral, until all were standing in silence. In the right aisle I saw a tall cross moving slowly above the heads of the people. Behind the cross came two tall, unlit candles. Fifteen feet behind the two candles was a six-foot tall, five inches thick, Easter candle. Behind that the staff and the mitre of the Cardinal could just be seen.

"It is Easter." Fiona was responding to Kate's question now that both were standing. "This is the celebration of the resurrection of Jesus."

Kate grew more restless. For years she had despised Christianity. She only used the name of Jesus in blasphemy. She was torn between an old desire to scorn the Christianity she had rejected and a new desire to know what it was that was calling to her.

The procession reached the back of the cathedral and congregated inside the entrance arch. Now the few lights that had been on in the cathedral were extinguished. The blackness that engulfed it was near total. It took my eyes over a minute to adjust before I could distinguish anything.

In the entrance nave, a fire was lit of very dry wood and soon it was crackling, lighting up the arch. All else remained in darkness. Gradually, everyone turned toward the entrance.

"Dear friends in Christ," the celebrant began the service. His voice was strong and confident. It was the Cardinal Archbishop of Westminster. He was dressed in vestments of white and gold. Ten other priests were in similar vestments. With them were numerous acolytes in their black cassocks and white surplices and the choir dressed in robes of red and white. All were standing around the fire.

The Cardinal continued. "On this most holy night our Lord Jesus Christ passed from death to life. We are invited to come together in vigil and prayer and to enter into the great mystery of his victory over sin and death."

Again at the name of Jesus, Kate fidgeted in reaction. "I don't like this," she thought. "I've got to get out of here." She noticed how agitated she was, and now the agitation was bringing back the darkness, the fear, the void. She would have left, but the darkness in the cathedral was so thorough she wouldn't have been able to find her way out.

Teshua raised his hands and placed them on Kate. He was praying, silently. "Purify and cleanse her mind. Give her hope, not fear."

"Let us pray." The Cardinal continued. "Father, we share in the light of your glory through your Son, the light of the world. Make this new fire holy, and inflame us with new hope. Purify our minds by this Easter celebration, and bring us, one day, to the feast of eternal light."

Kate seemed to calm down again.

"Christ, yesterday and today, the beginning and the end, Alpha and Omega. All time belongs to him and all the ages. To him be glory and power through every age and forever." The Cardinal continued. Now he took the large Easter candle and lit it from the flame. Then, from the Easter candle, the acolytes lit other candles and turned to the people standing nearby passing the flame. Soon there were hundreds of small candles burning brightly, chasing away the darkness in a small area in the back of the nave. The Cardinal again prayed, "May the light of Christ, risen in glory, dispel the darkness of our hearts and minds."

Teshua said, "The words are true. It is this light of Christ that has dispelled your darkness."

Suddenly, Kate smiled. She didn't know why. It was as though a heaviness was beginning to lift. She looked at Fiona who returned her smile. "My despair is gone, thank God," she thought. She was surprised at her own thought. "Thank God? When did I last think those words? When did I ever mean it?" Kate bowed her head in thought, and then made a decision. Under her breath she said, "Thank you." Then, she added, "…uh, Lord." Yes, the darkness was lifting and she suspected she might know why.

While Kate was lost in these thoughts, the Deacon raised the candle and sang out, "Christ our light!" In unison the crowd responded in song, "Thanks be to God." The Deacon, the Cardinal and all the priests, acolytes and the choir began a solemn procession down the nave.

As they moved forward, more and more people were lighting their candles from others around them. The candles gave light to the back half of the cathedral. The Deacon reached the centre of the nave and again he sang out in proclamation to all, "Christ our light." The sound rang from the entrance through the nave and up to the sanctuary. It filled the aisles and the chapels. In her mind Kate silently joined in the response. She had only heard the words and the tune once. "Thanks be to God."

The darkness in the cathedral was pushed into the corners. By the time the Deacon reached the stairs leading up into the sanctuary, over three thousand candles had been lit. The cathedral was filling with light.

"That's pretty cool." Thought Kate.

A third time, the Deacon sang out, "Christ our light." This time Kate held her breath and whispered the tune cautiously, trying to see how it would feel. "Thanks be to God." There was no fear, no agitation, but there was no great spiritual experience either. Kate exhaled, relieved.

Again, all grew quiet. The Deacon placed the Easter candle into a stand in front of the altar. He moved from there toward the pulpit from which he would sing "The Exultet", the great song in praise of the resurrection.

Michael turned to me and said, "Listen carefully now. You need to hear many things all at once."

The cathedral started growing brighter. I looked up at the lights, but they weren't on. The brightness was coming from the pews. It was the host of heaven. Each of the angels seemed to be taller and somehow brighter. From what I could see, their brightness was now beyond that of the candles. The angels raised their arms and prepared to sing, "Worthy is the lamb who was slain..." At that moment, the Deacon intoned: "Rejoice, oh heavenly powers! Sing choirs of angels! Exult, all creation around God's throne!"

The beauty of what I heard astounded me. It was as though my ears had developed the ability to taste and feel music, not just hear it. Of all the things that I saw and heard in the time I had with Michael, this is by far the most difficult to describe. Each of the angels was singing its own part, yet they were a perfect fit. Their voices were more than voices. They had the quality of particular musical instruments. The angel behind the Deacon most noticeably sounded like a trumpet. When the Deacon sang, "Salvation belongs to our God, who sits upon the throne," this angel simply sang the word "Salvation..." Both in his bodily demeanour and in the quality of his voice he seemed to be a herald sounding the trumpet. "Sal—vaaaa—tion!" The second syllable was held long and loud a third higher than the first syllable. The Deacon continued, "Jesus Christ our King is risen! Sound the trumpet of salvation!"

Other angels sounded like violins, clarinets, organs or countless other instruments—but instruments that sang words. One angel—and I must say, just one look at him and I knew what he would sound like—was a bassoon singing "Glory to God." The word "glory" was sung very low and strong on one note. It brought with it the essence of glory that could only be ascribed to God. I felt a kind of electricity passing through my flesh as I listened. I knew that I was hearing "glory," not just the word, but the reality.

It is difficult enough to define the word glory in such a way that it can carry the meaning it is meant to carry, that is, "God's nature." My experience was not just an intellectual one, although I did experience an understanding of glory that I had never had before. It was also a sensual one. My ears heard glory. My eyes were seeing it. My skin was feeling it. I was filled with a sense of awe.

Another angel was a singing flute. She, (I don't know anything about the gender of angels, but this one certainly seemed feminine), had a very lively melody that quickly danced through the scale as she sang (or played) "praise and glory and wisdom and thanks and honour and power and strength be to our God forever and ever." In her melody was a light-hearted rejoicing, utterly free of all cares. My chest seemed too small for my heart. It was full of joy and laughter like a smile I could not repress. I was feeling joy in my hands and feet. Even my joints were experiencing a light thrill of happiness. Oddly, the light-heartedness of this angel's song somehow took nothing away from the solemnity and the awe of the organ angel who was singing "Holy, holy, holy, Lord God of power and might. Heaven and earth are full of your glory. Hosanna in the highest." These two realities somehow blended perfectly. In fact, I was suddenly aware of all the different motifs: joy, awe, thanksgiving, and peace—a multitude of pleasures—all at once. As it says in Psalm 16, "In your presence there is fullness of joy, in your right hand are pleasures for evermore."

The organ angel, his voice—I should say voices—was/were in four parts. How can one voice sing a chord? I don't know, he did, and it was magnificent. It was overwhelming not because it was loud, but because it was so full. I couldn't believe that such a full sound could come from one angel. It was more than just sound. There was an aroma, an incense, as well. Unfortunately, I cannot describe the smell. I have never smelled anything like it. When I am hungry, there is nothing like the smell of frying chicken, or fresh bread from the oven. Those smells are enjoyable. What I smelled then was irresistible. I had to inhale it and then inhale it again. The aroma awakened a hunger for the Lord, the reason for this worship.

As each of my senses was being filled, I was beginning to understand what it meant to be totally engrossed in one thing. The worship being given by the angel that sounded like an organ occupied him fully. He was transfixed, by what he was doing. Completely undistracted, he entered into worship with all that he was. It showed in his countenance. Was he seeing the Lord, seated on the throne, in all his glory and splendour? I don't know, but I know of no definition of joy or fulfilment that can otherwise adequately describe what I saw in him at that moment.

Slowly, solemnly, and with great precision he sang: "Holy,…Holy,…Holy." Although that was all he sang I experienced the meaning of his words: there is none who is, in any way, like the Lord, Most High. I wanted to draw nearer to the Lord, yet I knew more than ever that I was unworthy. I had stumbled into the presence of One who is truly holy, and I had no right to be there. I felt like I might be trespassing. At the same time I knew that this was where I was meant to be. There was something so right about being there, but something so wrong about me. In that moment I was profoundly aware of the Lord's greatness and my own nothingness. I couldn't help but kneel and bow my head.

The deacon continued his song calling on earth to rejoice as well. "Rejoice, oh earth, in shining splendour, radiant in the brightness of your King!" As he sang, it was as though the walls and pillars of the cathedral began to take on some of the glory of the angels. The air itself seemed visible and alive. He continued, "Christ has conquered! Glory fills you! Darkness vanishes forever!" At the words "Christ has conquered" a great shout of victory went up from the angels in the midst of the song. Don't ask me how, but somehow the shout of victory fitted into the song perfectly, without diminishing the beauty of the harmony.

The effect of everything was perfection and completeness. The angels sang in many languages. They harmonised with one another, while blending impeccably with the Deacon who was singing "The

Exultet." I listened to one and then to another and then to all of it together.

In spite of all the complexity I have just described, it never ceased to be a very simple melody. At the time, I thought, "A child could sing this." It was as if I could anticipate each note, harmony, rhythm and word. I have tried, since then, to recreate what I heard, but I have concluded that it is impossible. It is like trying to describe the word "blue" using only numbers. They are such different things that even though both are simple, one just cannot be used to describe the other.

My watch registered that "The Exultet" lasted but ten minutes. For my soul it seemed like hours. Physically, I was refreshed in a way I never have been before.

"Michael, do you feel that?" I asked.

"In fact, no." He answered. "You seem to forget that I am an angel. I don't feel it, but I do understand and appreciate it, and far better than you do now. It is good."

My eye shifted to Kate. She heard the words, "Christ has conquered! Glory fills you! Darkness vanishes forever!" Suddenly, she thought back, remembering what she had intended to be her final night. "Christ conquered. Glory filled me. Darkness vanished. That is what happened to me!" For the first time she remembered calling out to God that night for help. "It was him. He heard me!" Again she wasn't left with much time to dwell on these thoughts. The Exultet had ended. People where blowing out their candles and being seated as some of the cathedral lights were turned on.

The vigil service continued with the reading of Scripture and the singing of psalms. Kate listened attentively. She would hear a reading and something about it would impress her. After thinking about it, she would come back to listening to what was being read, and again she would hear something that seemed to apply to her.

Teshua placed his hands on Kate's ears and prayed that she be given ears to hear. As he did, lector began the next reading, "They are happy, whose God is the Lord, the people he has chosen as his own." The grace of God again surrounded her—lights of many hues more abundant than ever.

The reading struck home. Kate knew it was true for her. "'They are happy, whose God is the Lord.' Why am I so happy tonight?" She wondered. "Could God be choosing me?...No," she thought, "I know better than that. Not with the life I have lived, but still, I am enjoying this."

The next reading was from Psalm 16. The words glued her to the pew, awestruck. "...My body rested in safety. For he did not leave my soul among the dead, nor let his beloved know decay. He will show me the path of life, the fullness of joy is in his presence, at his right hand happiness forever."

"My God, that was me. I should have been dead. My body should be decaying, but I'm not dead! In fact, I haven't felt this alive in years—maybe ever."

On it went, reading after reading struck the mark as Kate remembered what had just happened to her on Friday. Each time she found herself inhaling deeply as if she were breathing in new life, life as she had never known it. The whole service seemed put together just for her.

Isaiah 54—"You will have nothing to fear. Remote from terror, it will not approach you."...Psalm 29—"I will praise you Lord, you have rescued me and did not let my enemies rejoice over me. O Lord, you have raised my soul from the dead, restored me to life from those who sink into the grave...The Lord listened and had pity. The Lord came to my help."

...Isaiah 55—"Seek the Lord while he is still to be found, call to him while he is still near. Let the wicked man abandon his way. Let him turn back to the Lord who will take pity on him, to our God who is rich in forgiving; for my thoughts are not your thoughts, nor are my ways your ways—it is the Lord who speaks."

"What a fool I have been." She thought. She had thought that many times, but now it was different. She knew she needed her whole past to be dealt with somehow. It wasn't just regrettable. It was wrong. Words came to her mind. "Forgive me Lord." Again she fought back tears. The lector read on, "...so the word that goes forth from my mouth does not return to me empty, without carrying out my will and succeeding in what it was sent to do."

Everyone now stood as the Cardinal again prayed, but Kate remained seated. Teshua was convincing her of God's willingness to forgive even the greatest of sinners who repents. Kate again repeated the words, "Forgive me Lord."

At this, the lights in the cathedral suddenly came on fully. Bells began to ring throughout the sanctuary. The acolytes rapidly rang the high-pitched bells they held in their hands. Even the cathedral carillon rang out. Its bells were heavy. The bass rang long, low, deep. The tenor bells were ringing three times for every one of the bass's. The alto bells rang at a pitch on octave higher that the bass's but on the off beat. A variety of soprano bells were ringing rapidly, merrily. The effect was joyful, or so it seemed judging from the faces of the people. Many were smiling as the bells rang and rang. Then all, and as one, they stopped. Kate looked up, wiping away a tear. The entire congregation stood, "Glory to God in the highest!" was proclaimed by the chorus as it began singing "The Gloria." As I heard it, I couldn't help but think of the verse from scripture that says, "There is more rejoicing in heaven over the one sinner who repents than over the ninety-nine who are just."

Now another psalm was sung by the cathedral chorus, Psalm 117—"Give thanks to the Lord for he is good, for his love has no end. The Lord's right hand has triumphed…" Kate listened, simply enjoying the beauty of the music as it built and crescendoed toward the finish. "His right hand raised me up. I shall not die, I shall live and recount his deeds."

"This is amazing. I am going to have to tell someone about all this," thought Kate.

The Gospel of the Resurrection was now sung in all its glory followed by a homily acclaiming the truth of the resurrection.

The vigil continued with the renewal of baptismal promises. "Do you reject the glamour of evil and refuse to be mastered by sin?" Those who were around her were all saying in unison, "I do." Kate realised that this simply had not been true for her. She had loved the glamour of evil, and sin had become her master. The

Cardinal continued, "Do you reject Satan, Father of Sin and Prince of Darkness?" Again, the people responded, "I do."

"The Prince of Darkness," Kate thought. She shuddered, as a chill went through her. The sense of darkness and despair washed over her. "Go away!" she said in her mind, "Go away! I don't want this." Teshua repeated the question to her. "Do you reject Satan, Father of Sin and Prince of Darkness?" Now Kate responded, whispering, "I do. I want to turn away from it all." Teshua had become even brighter, quietly rejoicing in these moments for which he had worked for so long.

Throughout the Eucharistic prayer and communion Kate just sat and thought. The presence of the Lord was so real to her and so profound that she only wanted to rest in what she had so suddenly found after years of searching for it and hiding from it at the same time. After two and a half hours the vigil was about to end. All stood for the final prayers. Kate was as happy as she could ever remember. All night the Lord had ministered his love to her. The closing song was begun. She noted what a glorious melody it had but only on the second verse did she open her programme and see the words, "Awake oh sleeper, rise from the dead and Christ will give you light."

Awake oh sleeper, rise from the dead and Christ will give you light. There was no more accurate way that Kate could think of to summarise her own experience. The gratitude, the happiness, and the sense of forgiveness that she had been trying to control all night finally burst the emotions' dam. Kate's eyes filled with tears and she began to cry, openly.

Michael Shaughnessy

Fiona looked at Kate out of the corner of her eye and instinctively knew why Kate was crying. Her eyes also began to fill with tears. After a couple of minutes, Kate wiped away her tears and turned to Fiona. "Thank you." She said, "Thanks for bringing me."

"Welcome home!" said Fiona as she turned and hugged her sister.

"Happy Easter!" The greeting was being given by the Cardinal and the priests as the people left the cathedral. Fiona and Kate left by the centre aisle, both smiling. As they approached the priest at the door he looked at Kate's unusual appearance. His eyes opened just a bit wider. Then he saw her smile. He gave each of them a hand, nodded his head and said, "Christ is risen!" Fiona responded, "He is risen indeed!"

Outside, many were exchanging Easter greetings. Kate found herself saying it over and over to people she did not know and had never seen before, but her joy needed to be expressed.

The plaza was crowded. As Kate shook hands with someone after yet another Easter greeting, she turned and bumped into someone else. It was the Cardinal. He turned around as she said, "Sorry." Then abandoning all decorum she said, "Christ is risen" and gave him a hug. The Cardinal looked at the two priests beside him, slightly embarrassed, and then in his peaceful, stately tone of voice he said, "He is risen indeed," nodding his head and smiling as Kate turned away. She stopped and turned her head back, saying. "Oh, and...thanks!" Then she took Fiona by the arm and walked away.

People lingered in front of the cathedral talking to the many priests who served them. Slowly the casual conversations died out as people left. Inside the cathedral the wardens were left to pick up the programmes and candles and to straighten the chairs in anticipation of the 7:00 am service. All had to be set in order for those who would come to continue the celebration of the Resurrection of Christ. Still, it was nearly three in the morning before the cathedral was emptied. One by one the overhead lights were extinguished. Finally, only Michael and I were left in the huge stillness of the cathedral that was now lit by many candles, which would burn until dawn before they went out.

"That's a victory story." I said, once things had quieted down.

"Yes. There is more rejoicing in heaven…"

I completed the quotation from the scripture, "…over the one sinner who repents than the ninety-nine righteous who need no repentance."

"That is true also." Michael said. "However, had I finished, I would have said: there is more rejoicing in heaven yet to come."

I was not sure what Michael meant, and before I could ask, we were walking toward the chapel that bears his name. He again led as with a purpose.

CHAPTER 9:

THE END BEGINS

"Our time grows short. I will soon need to leave, but there is one more event I must explain."

"Which is…"

"The return of the Lord."

It struck me that I might be in a position to receive some highly coveted information. I decided to ask my questions from here on very carefully. "Do you know whether I will live to see the return of the Lord?" I asked.

Michael answered simply, "No."

I was disappointed, and asked why he didn't know.

"Because I don't know when the Lord will return."

I didn't give up. I still hoped to get some privileged information. "Is it the case that you know more than anyone but God himself about the Lord's return?"

"Among the angels I am the highest in the chain of command."

"Are you free to talk to me about what you know?"

"Oh, most definitely."

I tried to act detached, as though the subject might be only of some mild interest. "Given that you cannot answer the 'when' question, how about if I just ask you the standard 'who, what, where, why and how' questions?"

"Consider them asked." Michael replied and then began a long narrative that lasted until dawn. I have recorded here what I can remember, but I fear it only dimly reflects our late night conversation.

Currently, among the heavenly host, anticipation of the second coming is very high. I have not seen an atmosphere of expectation like this since the first coming. Many of us are reviewing our roles for the final day and getting prepared. There remains a final battle to be waged with Satan and his minions. Our planning these days is more and more about that final battle. My captains, who are making preparations, regularly ask me, 'Michael, have you heard anything more?' They know that the kind of preparations we are making in these days are unusually serious, of a type reserved for only the most significant of confrontations between the host of heaven and the hoards of hell.

The Angels of worship, those who stand before the throne night and day and never cease to sing, are more and more pleading to the Lord through the words of one Psalm in particular. It says,

'O Lord God of vengeance, oh God of justice shine forth. Rise up oh judge of the earth. Give the proud what they deserve. O Lord how long shall the wicked, how long shall the wicked triumph?'

They are longing to see the justice that will only come when Christ Jesus returns to reign on earth.

But it doesn't stop there. Yesterday I spoke again with Gabriel. The angels under his command bring the word of the Most High to the prophets. They usually are kept busy with a wide variety of things to say to the four corners of the earth. In these days the message is getting shorter, and clearer, and more consistent. 'A day of unprecedented battle is at hand. Prepare! Judgement has already begun, issue a call to repentance while there is yet the time, for the time grows short!'

In addition, even my own spirit is growing restless, not from lacking anything to do, but from eagerness for something great to do. That same restlessness is everywhere in heaven, and unlike any that I have seen before, and who is to say why?

However, before you jump to any conclusions I should note that serious preparations have always been part of our battle planning. The present time of darkness warrants serious preparation, even if this is not the time of the final battle. Still, I will describe what I know of the second coming, regardless of when it will be.

In the fullness of time, when the final day does come, all worship before the throne will stop. Silence will fall as the Father stands. The entire heavenly host will kneel. Last of all, even the Son will kneel before his Father to receive his final commission. What exactly the Father will say I do not know, but I do know what he has said to the prophets about that day and I expect what he will say to the Son will be similar...

'Who rises up for me against the wicked? Who stands up for me against evildoers? Today I make the nations your heritage, and the ends of the earth your possession. Break them with a rod of iron, and dash them in pieces like a potter's vessel. Kings shall see and arise; princes shall fall prostrate before you, because I, the Lord, the faithful, the Holy One of Israel, have chosen you.

'Behold you are my servant, whom I uphold, my chosen, in whom my soul delights; I have put my Spirit upon you to bring forth justice to the nations. I am the Lord, I have called you in righteousness, I have taken you by the hand and kept you; I have given you as a covenant to the people, a light to the nations, to open the eyes that are blind, to bring out the prisoners from the dungeon, and from the prison those who sit in darkness.

'Blow the trumpet in Zion; sound the alarm on my holy mountain! Let all the inhabitants of the land tremble, for the day of the Lord is at hand. Advance, oh horses. Rage, oh chariots! Prepare for war! Stir up the mighty! Let all the host of heaven draw near. Come! Beat your plowshares into swords, and your pruning hooks into spears; let even the weak say, I am a warrior. Let the warriors go forth: those who handle the shield, those skilled in handling the bow. Let justice roll down like waters, and righteousness like an ever-flowing stream. This is a day of darkness and gloom, a day of clouds and thick darkness! Like blackness there will spread upon the mountains a great and powerful host, like there has never been from of old, nor will be again through the years of all generations. Fire will devour all before them, and behind them a flame will burn. A day of wrath is this day, a day of distress and anguish, a day of ruin and devastation, a day of darkness and gloom, a day of clouds and thick darkness, a day of trumpet blast and battle cry against my enemies in their fortified cities and their lofty battlements.

'Arise, in your anger, lift yourself up against the fury of my enemies; for I have appointed a judgement. Rule in the midst of your foes!'

At that moment the age of mercy shall end and the age of justice shall begin.

There is a robe, kept in heaven. It is red. It has been dipped in blood, and on it is written: *King of Kings and Lord of Lords*. On that great and terrible day I will place that robe on the shoulders of the Son of Man. I also will present to him his sword, the Sword of the Spirit which is called the Word of God, quoting the Psalm, 'O mighty one, gird your sword upon your thigh. In glory and majesty ride forth in victory for the cause of truth and to defend the right.'

After a period of silence, the Son will rise, and for the first time since he ascended to heaven and sat down at the right hand of the Father, he will leave the throne room and prepare for war.

The saints too will now don their battle garments, linen white and pure, and then report to heaven's stables. Here there are countless horses, each of them a white stallion trained for war. They are eager for battle, pawing and snorting. The saints will saddle their horses, and assemble in battle array before the gates of heaven. It will be a great multitude: men and women from every tribe and language, every people, race and tongue, from every age and every generation, young and old—all those who, through faith, have persevered.

Then Jesus, riding a mighty white stallion, will take his place at the head of the heavenly host and he will quote—not the words of Paul: 'Oh death, where is your terror? Oh death where is your sting?'—instead it will be the words of the prophet Hosea: 'Oh death, I am your plague. Oh death, I am your destruction!' The time will now have come for those words to be fulfilled. The last enemy, death, once defeated, is now to be destroyed.

On earth all will wonder at what next takes place. The sun will grow dark and the moon will no longer reflect its light. The sky will grow darker than ever before and stars will begin falling from the sky.

Meanwhile, in heaven, I will address the gate and its keeper, 'Lift up your heads oh gates and be lifted up oh ancient doors for the King of Glory.'

The gate keeper will lift his voice and ask, 'Who is this King of Glory?'

'The Lord strong and mighty, the Lord mighty in battle!' I will reply. But then I will command with a loud voice, 'Lift up your heads oh gates and be lifted up oh ancient doors. It is the Lord of Hosts. He is the King of Glory!'

At this the gates of heaven will open. As they do, Gabriel will lift a trumpet to his lips. The blasts from his trumpet will be a call to war that will shake the very foundations of heaven and earth. Those who are awake will wonder where the sound is coming from. Those indoors will run outside. Those out of doors will look for the source, but they will not see it. Those who are asleep will be stirred from even the deepest slumber and rub their eyes, amazed by the sound and wondering what it could mean. Over and over again the call will be sounded until every man, woman, and child is awake.

When the trumpet blast ends, in heaven a loud shout will go up that will be audible on earth, 'Hallelujah, for the Lord our God the Almighty reigns! Behold your God! Behold your God comes with power!'

Next, the Lord of Hosts will appear riding a white charger—neck and limbs, muscles, bones and sinews all straining ahead eager for battle. Following behind him, arrayed in all their glory, will be all the angels of heaven and all who have died in Christ. All those who dwell on the earth will shield their eyes before the glory of heaven.

You have yet to see the glory of an angel. We are light, brilliant light, blazing like a thousand suns, painfully bright. You would not be able to look directly at us because of the brilliant intensity of our splendour. Our voices are like thunder even when we whisper. We are more majestic than the mountains and more magnificent than the sea. Our presence will be more terrifying than the angel of death...and more comforting than the quiet of the stillest night—depending on the disposition of the heart.

Yes, as the heavens empty, terror or comfort will appear on every face as they behold myriads and myriads of angels. Thousands upon thousands will pour forth through the gates and fill the sky with glory. Even so, we will not be that to which every eye is drawn. We will be dull in comparison to the Son of Man appearing for the first time in the fullness of his glory. Ours is but a reflected glory. As the sun outshines the moon, so the Lord outshines us. On a brilliant day you can barely see the moon because of the brightness of the sun even though it is high in the sky.

If it is painful for you to look at the sun, and angels are more brilliant than the sun, and thousands upon thousands of angels will be there, and the Lord outshines them all such that they are dim in comparison, you might be wondering how you will be able to bear such a sight. I will tell you a mystery. You will be changed—in a flash—in the twinkling of an eye when Gabriel blows the trumpet. The perishable will clothe itself in the imperishable; the mortal shall put on immortality. You are going to be transformed and given a spiritual body equipped with eyes to look upon beauty unimaginable. But don't be distracted by this transformation of your body, rather stand up, lift your head and behold the return of the Holy One of Israel.

Now the judgement of the nations will begin. It will begin with grace for the righteous. The hands of the deaf shall rush to their ears in wonder as they hear for the first time. The feeble and the paralysed will momentarily lose control over their bodies. They will be astonished as their broken bones are mended, their twisted spines are straightened, their gnarled hands are made supple, as unceasing pains cease, and as incurable conditions are cured. Their limbs will fill with warmth and tingling as circulation and nerves are restored. The lame and crippled will rise from their chairs and walk.

Those who are dumb suddenly will speak. Motor control will be given to their tongues. Larynxes will be restored. Words will form in their minds and be spoken through their lips. They will be astounded as they hear sounds coming from their own mouths. The eyes of the blind shall be opened in an instant. They will see colour and motion, texture and shape, height and depth for the first time. What can they do but shout and sing?

Grace will be extended to all creation. Birds will begin to warble for joy, all in harmony with one another—a symphony of sopranos. Robin will call to the owl, 'Awake! Awake and sing. Sing a new song in praise of the king who comes to redeem the earth. Our travail is ended. Again we will sing the harmony of heaven.'

Sheep, wolves, fox and deer will sing the tenor's tune together. Cattle, horses, lion and buffalo will join in, basses lending an eager affirmation. Trees will rattle their leaves like snare drums. The winds will play a bush like a flute. The seas will come alive, as countless fish break for the surface of the waters, eager to see the coming king. Schools of fish will dance in unison and whales will leap high above the surface of the deep, twisting and turning and falling back into the water with a slap.

Even the dead in their graves shall be stirred by the sound of the trumpet, for it will be a call to them to awake from their sleep. Tombs will be opened as the multitudes of those trapped in death begin to experience the same power that raised Christ from the dead now flowing through whatever remains of their sinews, bones and flesh. Ashes strewn across the waters will be drawn back together. Matter will be reshaped and reformed to provide muscle, organs and tissues. Senses that long lay dormant will be reawakened. The resurrection of the dead will be happening in every graveyard, cemetery and mausoleum in all nations, in each of their cities, and all their villages.

But, alas for Satan and his allies on this day, for this is the day of the Lord, a day of terror. As the sky grows dark and the trumpet sounds Satan will know his hour has come. That which he has dreaded for aeons will finally be upon him. This source of fear, this author of horror, the father of evil, wickedness and sin will cower as he faces his own destruction. The very gates of hell will shake as the Lord descends to judge sin, death and all that is evil.

Once again the Lord will come face to face with Satan. But this time it will not be just as a man, 'weak and helpless'. It will be as the Son of Man, in all his glory, majesty and power.

In his great pride, Satan will resist him with every ounce of rebellion, stubbornness and hatred within him, making his deceit-filled claims to glory.

'So…' He will begin. 'You have come. Am I to be impressed with this show of power? Does your majesty fill me with awe? You should know better! Do you expect me to do homage before you? I have reigned on earth since the beginning. Since the dawn of humanity I have been the master. I am the Prince of this world! I am the Lord of this world of sin. I am the King of Darkness! I do not bow before man! You bow to me! It is my wisdom that reigns on earth. Who is the one all-powerful on earth? I AM! Who has held out against my power of temptation? Who has not yielded to sin? No, you must bow before me!'

Thunder will crash and bolts of darkness will explode from Satan's upraised hands.

The Son of Man will remain standing, undeluded by the deceit, undaunted by the power, unmoved by the words and works of darkness. In simple, yet absolute authority, with no show of power, the Son of Man will raise his right hand in judgement, and with one finger pointed upward, he will say, 'Your reign is ended...'

Satan will interrupt: 'You demand that I submit, but I will not submit! I will not serve! I will not kneel!'

The Son of Man will refuse to be interrupted, 'Your power is broken...'

Even so, Satan will argue, 'You are a man! I am an angel! I will not bow. I will not bend the knee. I will not worship. I will not speak your name or acknowledge your glory.'

Yet even as he speaks Satan will know his powers of darkness have finally failed. Slowly, painfully, he will collapse to his knees before a truth he refuses to believe. And then he, himself, on bended knee, with his own tongue will confess, 'Let all the heavens and the earth declare, to the glory of God the Father, that Jesus Christ is Lord!'

Then he will hear the words of his eternal judgement: 'You are cursed forever, depart into the everlasting fire prepared for you.'

In that moment, with the truth admitted and the judgement given, the authority of evil will be broken and the powers of darkness destroyed for all time. Sin and death will fail, and the glorious and eternal reign of Jesus Christ, the King of Kings and Lord of Lords over a new heavens and a new earth, will fully and finally begin!

Michael's eyes seemed to fill with tears of joy. "Do angels cry?" I wondered. I suspect not, but I can recognise joy. Even more, I can recognise a loyal, fierce love when I see it. I was seeing it.

"Is that day near?" Michael continued. "I cannot say. Is it far off? No...

"Only recently the armies of heaven have been given battle orders for which we are to prepare. They are our final assignments for the day of the Lord. Each of us now knows what we are to do on that day. For now, we continue to fight as we always have, but there is a difference. In these days we fight with our ears ready to hear a command which will alter..."

At this Michael paused and dropped his head to listen. After a brief moment he stood and turned toward me. "Unfortunately I must leave. The Most High has summoned me. He has called a meeting of the High Council of Heaven regarding a matter of great urgency and I must attend. War is at hand. The armies of heaven are ready."

I instantly asked, "And those of earth?" Even as I asked, there was a bright flash of light where Michael stood. At first, it filled the entire chapel, and then just as quickly, it condensed into a brilliant point of light that accelerated out of the chapel into the nave leaving a brief trailing light. I watched as it soared upward into the heights of the cathedral with the sound of rushing air. As it reached the roof, it vanished. Michael was gone.

I sat, stunned. I don't know if it was hours or minutes later that I heard the sound of the cathedral doors opening. It was time for the sunrise resurrection service. It was time for me to go home and write down what I had seen and heard.

CHAPTER 10:

ON ANGELS AND PHYSICS

Lunch at McDonald's

Following Michael's explanation of the return of the Lord, I was convinced I wouldn't see him again. I was wrong. We met one more time. It was on my next visit to London.

I was walking from the Gatwick Express terminal at Victoria Station to catch the tube to a hotel somewhere in my company's budget category. My flight was seven hours late in arriving from Minneapolis. We were two hours delayed in take off due to mechanical failure. During what was supposed to be a brief stop in Boston, the decision was taken to change planes in order to properly repair what was not "quite fully repaired in Minneapolis." We were assured that we were never in any danger during the flight. In spite of that assurance one passenger grew paranoid about flying—she refused to continue the flight. After a half hour trying to talk her into flying anyway, the airline finally gave up, removed her luggage, and sent her home to Minot, North Dakota on a bus. We eventually continued our journey having lost another two hours and our take off slot. We then waited one hour on the run-way in the take-off queue, landed at Shannon Airport instead of Gatwick waiting for the fog to clear in Sussex and finally arrived to a weak

"Hallelujah Chorus", mixed with some of the worst language I can remember hearing in a public place.

My body still had that bloated feeling in the feet and legs that comes from sitting up all night digesting bomb-bay beef with baby onions, mashed potatoes, California claret and petits fours at thirty-five thousand feet. That was complemented by the empty feeling in my head from reading yesterday's Daily Telegraph and watching a movie that ran one week in the cinema and flopped, but was doomed to be shown for a month on North-worst Airlines flights to London at three a.m. Greenwich Mean Time as entertainment for the brain dead. By the time I reached Victoria Station it was three o' clock in the afternoon and I had been up for 26 hours.

As might be expected I was in a less than sociable mood. I had concluded that Attila the Hun was probably just misunderstood. He had really terrorised all Europe simply to deal with life's little frustrations. I stopped and thought about taking a similar approach to the airlines, when I was addressed from behind.

"You are going the wrong way."

I recognised the voice immediately, dropped my bags to the floor, and turned around.

"You are going the wrong way." He repeated. It was Michael.

"I don't think so," I said, "I'm going to the District Line. It's right there." I pointed at the sign that confirmed my accuracy: "District and Circle Lines."

"You are still going the wrong way." Michael picked up my bags and started walking with them. "You should be leaving via this exit." Michael was walking toward the Victoria Street exit. "You have a room at the Victoria Street Hotel for tonight and an appointment with me tomorrow."

"What about the appointment I have with Thomas Cook Travel tomorrow?"

"I already did your work, and got a better deal than you would have. The papers are waiting in your room. You and I will meet tomorrow at noon in the same place as usual. The following day you can get back on your intended schedule."

We reached Victoria Street. He hailed a taxi, put my cases in the boot, and said to the taxi driver, "The Victoria Street Hotel."

I got into the taxi and sat down, expecting Michael to join me. Instead of joining me, he just stuck in his head and said, "Go get some sleep. You will need a clear mind tomorrow." He closed the door and waved the taxi to take me to the Victoria Street Hotel.

As he said, the papers were there, waiting for my signature. I rang the headquarters of Thomas Cook to confirm the deal that we were making with them. They confirmed it and proposed I come in with the signed papers at my convenience. Michael had done it all by letter.

I fell into bed exhausted. For ten hours I imitated the sculpture of the Duke of Wellington on the sarcophagus in St. Paul's Cathedral, except I made more noise. I arrived at Westminster Cathedral just before noon.

Having discussed with Michael the Archangel some of the key events in salvation history and a few others beside I was clear that he knew what he was talking about. He even knew what I was talking about before I was talking about it. However, there is one area where he was totally lacking in understanding, culture and sophistication. His knowledge of the human palate was seriously underdeveloped.

"May I buy you lunch?"

"What manner of greeting is this?" I responded, reminded of Mary's response to Gabriel. I had grown used to questions from Michael that surprised me, but they were usually of a personal sort. (Not that lunch isn't personal. If it's not personal, it's not lunch.) By now I had become much more comfortable with talking to an angel about any number of things, but how are you supposed to react when an angel offers to buy you lunch? I was surprised. It is difficult enough for me to say yes or no to offers of hospitality, but when an angel asks you...

Michael pressed on, "It is a serious proposal. May I buy you lunch?"

"Lunch?" I asked, trying to delay in hopes of digging up a good answer.

"Yes, lunch."

I hadn't bought much time, and still didn't know what to say. "Buy more time." I thought. "Where?" I asked.

"McDonald's."

It was another one word answer that bought me no time, and added to my difficulties. Lunch was one thing, but McDonald's? There are many nice little delicatessens around Victoria Station, not to mention the pubs. I only went to McDonald's during Lent. I was still unclear about how I should respond. I delayed again. "You're not hungry, are you?" I asked. "This angel has no taste," I thought.

205

"You're right on both counts, I'm not and I don't."

"Not and don't what?"

"I am not hungry and I have no taste in food. Unfortunately, it is most certain that you will get hungry during our next discussion, so I have decided to avoid having to interrupt that discussion by buying you lunch in the place where you normally go during Lent, McDonald's. It was also a means to introduce the area we next need to discuss, which is 'Why angels have no taste in food.'"

"But I only went to McDonald's because it *was* Lent!" I answered. "I do it for self-denial only."

"All the better." Michael responded.

"He hasn't much feel for hospitality, either." I thought, but somehow that didn't seem to register on Michael's radar, or if it did, he ignored it.

We went to McDonald's. It led to a conversation with Michael that I didn't understand. I don't blame it on the food either. I still don't understand it very well. Oh, parts of it are perfectly clear, but some of it is too mathematical and philosophical for me to understand very well. I have written it down as best I can remember it, but I am almost certain I have some of it wrong.

I ordered some sort of *Mac-burger-meal* and we sat down at a white, plastic table. I opened my French fries and popped one into my mouth. "So, why don't angels have any taste in food?" I asked.

"Grace."

I laughed and said: "Especially if you have to eat here! No taste buds would make these easier to eat." I held up some fries for demonstration.

"No, you missed my point," said Michael. "Aren't you going to say grace before you eat?"

"In McDonald's?"

"Is it food?"

"Debatable," I thought as I bowed my head.

On Time and Eternity

"Angels have no taste in food because they are immaterial beings." Michael began.

"Right," I said, staring at my double or triple something-burger, wishing I were an angel.

"I will explain that later. The subject of our discussion today is matter, time, and space."

"Oh, no!" I thought, "There are worse things in life than lunch at McDonalds."

"Have you ever asked, 'How big is infinite? Or how long is eternal?'"

"Yes," I said, "hasn't everyone?"

"Exactly…Today, I am going to give you the answers."

(I almost choked on my Mac-burger. Of course, I usually do anyway, but this had caught me by surprise.)

Michael continued, "Let's start with time, and then we will move on to eternity. How would you define time?"

I thought for a moment while swallowing and then, using a French fry to demonstrate I took a stab at a definition. "It is like a line made up of the past, the present and the future in which the past is everything already done, the present is what is happening now, and the future is everything that will happen. How is that?" Certain that I had failed again, I ate my prop.

"A reasonable start," said Michael. Then he inquired, "When does a cheeseburger taste its best?"

"What?"

"When does a cheeseburger taste its best?"

"That sounds like the start of a joke an eleven year-old would tell."

"Does it taste best in the past, the present or the future?"

"I can only taste it in the present. Fortunately, that won't last long. In the current case it will soon be just a recent, relatively unpleasant memory."

"Exactly my point."

"How would you know that cheeseburgers leave a relatively unpleasant memory?" I asked.

"I was not referring to your cheeseburger. I was referring to the fact that the present moment is very short. Infinitely short. It is virtually non-existent. Do you understand?"

"No." I said, watching some sort of special sauce ooze into the styrofoam container as I lifted my lunch for its second assault on my taste buds.

"Once you understand that the present moment is infinitely short, you will see how difficult it is to prove that you exist."

"I thought the problem at hand is proving that you exist, not that I exist! I think I need an explanation."

"Yes. Let's start by looking at the present. How long is the present moment?"

"Well…"

"What are you thinking of right now." Michael snapped his fingers on the word "now."

"Let me see…"

"Don't bother. You are too late. That 'now' moment is already past. Here comes another one…right…now!" Again he snapped his fingers. "But it too, is already gone…You see; the present moment is very short. You can divide time down into smaller and smaller bits so that a nano-second is a long time. The time line is made up of an infinite number of points, or successive occurrences of 'the present' that have no dimension. They are infinitely small, impossible to measure. Normally, when you are thinking about the present, you are mostly considering the recent past and anticipating the very near future. The true 'present' hardly exists. I'll give you another example. Do you understand how a film is shot?"

That was a subject I did understand. I answered, "Yes, a camera takes, say, 32 individual pictures in one second. When they are played back at that speed, it looks like continual motion, but it is not. It is a succession of snap shots strung together."

"Exactly, each picture captures a moment in time. Now if you could take an infinite number of snap shots per second of, say, a running horse, you would have a better understanding of what it was doing at any 'moment of time.' However, even if you could develop such snap shots instantly, it would not 'prove' that the horse exists *now*, but only that it existed in the moment captured on film. Verifying the past is easier than verifying the present. However, it is only natural, having verified the immediate past to then jump to the conclusion that the horse continues to exist. But just because it existed a moment ago does not prove that it will continue to exist. It would be much harder to make this assumption if horses were in the habit of disappearing in an instant."

"Thank God," I said. "People are insecure enough about the future. They don't need to be worrying about going out of existence every second."

"You should do that more often."

"What? Worry about going out of existence?"

"No, thank God. You said, 'Thank God.' You should do that more often. However, I don't want to digress into a discussion of your prayer life. Let's get back to past, present and future. Give me your best definition of eternity."

I thought a bit, and said, "The Church and the Bible teach that we can have eternal life, so I suppose it means we live forever. Time will just keep on ticking by."

"That is one way to look at it but it is mono-directional. Try again."

"OK, how about time without beginning or end; you could look down the time line both ways forever. Something that lasts forever in both directions is eternal."

"That is better, but it still is rather weak. It is one-dimensional. Eternity isn't just a time line with both ends running on forever. A certain amount of eternity didn't roll by before the Most High created the universe. Putting eternity onto a time line doesn't work. You get closer to understanding eternity or infinite time by making it both three dimensional and non-dimensional."

"Of course, that must be right!" I said with feigned enthusiasm. "Only I don't have any idea what you mean." I looked at my chocolate Mac-shake and decided to wait longer, sucking mud through a straw is difficult. It is best to wait until the iced-non-dairy-substance thins down to a consistency a little more fluid than wood glue.

"First let's make time three dimensional. Pick a date."

"OK, April thirtieth, 1952." (My birthday seemed like a good enough date.)

"Now suppose you could go back in time and relive that date."

"No thanks, it was tough enough as it was, and I wouldn't want to put my mother through that again." Michael again ignored my attempt at humour.

"*If* you could go backwards in time, that would break one of the laws of time and space. Now in addition, what if you could not just go backward and forward on the time line, but you could go up, down and across it, so that time stood still and you could go exploring a particular moment in time? For example, suppose you could return to exactly two o'clock on April thirtieth, 1952 over and over again. First you could visit the hospital where you were born, and then you could visit Parliament to see what they were debating. Then you could check on what Joseph Stalin was having for lunch and finally you could check in on the seventh inning of the Yankees—Red Sox game."

"That would be interesting, but it would take a lot of time."

"In fact it would take no time at all. You would have to be outside of linear time in order to be able to do it. That is how the Most High sees time. He is not inside of it. To be eternal as the Most High is eternal, is to be outside of linear time altogether, to be able to look at all time at once: past, present and future."

"That must be why you can't fool God."

"It's one of the reasons."

"When I was young I tried working that one out. I would sit at my desk intending to fool God. I would say, 'I am going to raise my right hand off the table' and then, in a sudden motion raise my left instead. Of course I would figure out that God knew what I was thinking all along. Even a quick change of mind wouldn't surprise him. Even if I meant to raise my right hand and my motor control somehow was momentarily messed up and I raised my left, God would have seen it coming anyway. Omniscience always seemed to me to be an unfair advantage in playing 'Let's see if I can fool you.'"

"So you have the basic idea."

"Yes, time could be said to exist in three dimensions. I can measure it more than just linearly." I paused briefly and then asked a question. "Michael, let me see if I am understanding something correctly. If God is like you say, then he knows everything in advance, or he has absolute foreknowledge. He knows everything before it happens. Even my eternal destiny."

"From one point of view, yes."

"So am I going to go to heaven or hell?"

On Foreknowledge and Free Will

Michael paused a moment.

I waited with abated breath. My heart started to beat at a faster rate than normal as I realised how important this question was that I just asked. "Well…?" I prompted.

"Yes is your answer."

Clouds of confusion appeared on my mind's horizon. "Yes, what?"

"Yes, your eternal destiny is heaven or hell. Those are the only two options."

"But I was wondering if you knew my specific destiny!" My voice was slightly raised. Again, Michael took his time answering.

"No. I cannot see into the future except as I am informed by the Most High."

I was disappointed by his answer, but then my mind caught on to something he said. I noted, "So you can see into the past?"

"Yes, I am not time bound in the way you are, yet I am not outside of time altogether as is the Most High. Therefore I could tell you most anything you want to know, about anything that happened, at any past moment in time, anywhere in all of creation— although, I would need to do some research first."

"Maybe I can still get some worthwhile information," I thought, scrolling through my past for a significant event but nothing of note appeared, and before I could ask a question, Michael continued. "Unfortunately for you, that is not our purpose."

"Rats!" I said facetiously, "I've always wanted to know whether Bobby Williams cheated in a poker game when we were 14. I had a full house and he had four…"

"My apologies, but we were talking about foreknowledge and free will." Michael reminded me.

"OK. Here is a question for you. If it's already known for certain whether I will go to heaven or hell, why should I bother doing anything about it? It would appear that I have no role to play in determining my own future."

"You have asked a good question. How is it possible for there to be both an unchangeable destiny and personal accountability for what you do? This is mainly an issue of looking at the question from two different perspectives. From one perspective it appears that all things are already determined and will not change. From another, that you have free will. From the point of view of the Most High, everything is already finished; there is no change to come, no surprises, and no alterations. Everything is known, but that is not true from your point of view. From your point of view what you do, makes all the difference."

"How can that be?" I asked as I picked up my 'Hot Apple Pie', which was now a cold apple pie.

"What is in one of those things?" Michael asked.

I was just about to take my first bite. I stopped. I was growing used to Michael's sudden changes of direction. He wasn't asking this question because he was curious about fruit pies. He was going somewhere with this. I just didn't know where. I read him my answer from the package: "Flour, butter, sugar, eggs, baking powder, salt, corn syrup and apples, oh, and preservatives...Preservatives? This isn't about preservatives is it?" I thought that would be a very strange way to explain much of anything.

"No, it is not about preservatives. The destiny of the flour, butter, sugar, eggs, baking powder, salt, corn syrup, apples and preservatives was to become that apple pie and so it is. Once it was completed, its fate was sealed: apple fruit pie. It is not possible for it to have been something else. The time when it might have been say a cherry fruit pie is already past. There is no changing the past. However, what if they had put cherries in it?"

"I wouldn't have ordered it. I don't like cherries."

"You are missing the point of my question."

"Oh...Uh...then it would have been a cherry fruit pie."

"Right, but they didn't and so it is an apple fruit pie. That fruit pie can no longer be a cherry fruit pie. It could have been earlier, but not now. Looking at anything from the present perspective means: it is what it is, and cannot be other. Looking at the past from the present is the perspective of completion. You exist outside of the past. You can look upon it and make secure judgements. What is done is done; there is no changing it. The Most High's view of all time is one of completion. He is outside of the time line, so he can see all that was, is and will be, at once. He knows what has happened, what is happening, and what will happen. He can look upon it and make secure judgements."

"So he knows everything. That still doesn't answer why I should pray. It seems to me that if everything is determined, there is no reason to pray. Why pray? He isn't going to change his mind. Doesn't that mean prayer is useless."

"If you existed in the frame of reference of the Most High, that would be true, but you don't. Let's look at your prayer question from both perspectives, his and yours. That should help make the difference clearer."

"OK."

"Suppose you are trying to decide whether or not to pray for an increase in your salary so that you can send your children to college. Finally, you actually pray. Also suppose that the Most High chooses to act in your favour and on that basis moves your employer to say, 'yes' instead of 'no'. If you hadn't prayed, you wouldn't have received the increase. This is an example of the normal way that you think in your current time frame. Your actions make a difference. The Most High hears your prayers. Your choices affect the outcome of your life. Now, put yourself into the eternal time frame. From the point of view of the Most High, your prayer was always known, always answered and your employer moved. There was never any question. The whole of the time line was seen, past, present and future. All outcomes are already known and determined."

"But what if I hadn't prayed?"

"Then that would have been what happened and the outcome would have been just as certain. That would have been what was seen from above the time line. You would not have prayed, your employer would not have been moved, and you would have received no pay increase. There are no surprises in the eternal time frame of the Most High. What you have done, what you are doing and what you will do are all known. In the eternal now of the Most High, all things are known. They are predestined and cannot change. This is more than foreknowledge. Foreknowledge implies time. But for the Most High there is no time.

For him what is, is. For you who exist in time and space—in the present, as you would call it—all your choices in life are free. For the Most High, all your choices are facts. He knows what is. But he never made your decisions for you. You were and are always free to choose one option or another."

Omnipresence and the One Act of Being

"Now let's work on another of the original questions, 'Where was the Most High before the universe was created.' We have dealt with the 'before' problem, now let's deal with the 'where' problem, what do you think 'omnipresence' means?"

"It means that God is everywhere at once. He is big enough to cover all creation and he is fully present everywhere."

"That is an interesting definition. Let me see what you mean by it."

"Now I'm in trouble." I thought.

"Your image is that of a being so large that he covers everything and is in everything."

"Yes."

"Is the very part of this being which is in New York also here in London?"

"Uh...no, it can't be in two places at once."

"Then this being is not fully present everywhere."

"I changed my mind. Yes, that which is in New York is also in London."

"How?"

I ran my fingers through my hair and then took a sip of coffee hoping that might yield an inspiration. It didn't. "I don't know, you tell me."

"Your definition of omnipresence is inaccurate for starters. Omnipresence **does mean** the ability to be present to all creation, that is, to be everywhere, and it is the ability to be *fully* present, not just partly present, to all creation. However, size has nothing to do with omnipresence. The Most High doesn't need to be 'big enough' to be everywhere. His ability to be everywhere has more to do with his existing outside of time than his size. Because the Most High is not bound by time, he can be present at any point in time. He can visit any point on the time line. If you again take the thirtieth of April 1952, at two o'clock exactly, it is possible for the Most High to visit anything in the universe at that moment of time. He not only can be, but is fully present in all these places as well."

"Like you said earlier, he could be at the hospital, Parliament, Joseph Stalin's lunch and the Yankees' game…Hold on a moment. You said he not only can be, but *is* present in all places."

"Yes."

"As in every molecule? He is fully present in every atom?"

"Exactly. As far as science is concerned, material creation is made of a huge number of very small particles. If you personally had an infinite amount of time it would be possible to visit each particle as it were."

"A bit like a doctor making house calls,…but to every particle in creation?"

"For one with an infinite amount of time, that is no problem. However, you must remember that it is not as if he only manages to visit every one of them in the course of several thousand years. He can visit every one of them in the smallest division of time. Literally, no time goes by between his visits. In every moment of time he visits every one of them and 'touches' them, as it were. It is this touch that keeps them going, that keeps them existing. Without this, they would cease to be."

"It's like one of those old variety shows where people spun plates on top of six foot poles. They had to tap each one every so often or they would lose their momentum and fall to the ground, shattering into hundreds of pieces."

Michael didn't seem impressed by the analogy. He continued. "Every particle of matter is given the energy, the power to continue in existence by this infinite series of 'divine touches.' Without them, all material creation would disappear in a single moment."

"Can you explain what you mean by this divine touch? I sure don't feel anything, but then maybe I am just used to it? Is that it?"

"Not exactly. In a sentence, it is the divine touch, or power from the Most High that creates all matter and then keeps it all in being by giving it the power or ability to exist. Without this touch, all things would cease to exist."

"That is a nice definition. What does it mean?"

"It means that if you were broken down into your smallest constituent parts, you would find that you teeter between being energy and matter. You could lose all your matter and turn into energy.

"Matter in its smallest form has some interesting properties. It is like light in that respect. Light has some of the properties of matter, and some of the properties of a wave of energy. Is it matter or is it energy? At the most basic level they are nearly indistinguishable. Matter is always on the brink of turning back into energy and energy back into matter. It is at this level that the Most High transforms his existence into what you call matter. It is a function of his omnipotence. His power, his energy he transforms into matter, and the energy that holds matter together. If he were to stop willing this to be, both matter and energy would disappear. Fortunately, he doesn't. Ultimately, when you get down to this level, it is obvious that all things are given their being from the Most High. The divine touch is his infinite existence transformed into a finite amount of matter and energy, in a finite number of moments in time."

"That almost sounds like the basis for the Big Bang. A huge amount of energy is supposed to have been turned into a huge amount of matter in the first moment of time."

"That is the theory."

"Is it the correct understanding of what happened?"

"To some degree, yes. However, I would remind you that what was considered to be certain in one age was proven to be not the best explanation in succeeding ages. The same will be true about modern astronomy. The present laughs at the certainties of the past, and so your great grandchildren will laugh at the certainties of today. Copernicus was wrong about some things but he was more right than his predecessors. The same is true for Galileo, Newton, and Einstein."

"What would happen if God quit? Would everything instantly revert back to nothing? Would all matter and energy, including me, no longer exist?

Would it be like the Big Bang in reverse: the Big Unbang?"

"In theory, yes."

"Why, 'in theory?'"

"If we all ceased to exist, it would be difficult for us to prove we went out of existence."

"I see your point."

"Now, if we review what we have covered so far, that will help in understanding the next point where we put it all together. First, I noted that the present is infinitely short, indeed, without dimension. Secondly, I explained how time can be looked at as three dimensional, not just linear. It became infinitely big. You could cut across the timeline and review all the events that were happening at any given point in time for as long as you liked. Finally, we considered how the Most High is omnipresent, that is fully present to everything. Now the next thing to understand about the Most High that he has no past and no future. He, unlike us, exists only in the present, or to put it in its formal terms, he exists in one act of being."

"One act of being?"

"Yes."

"You lost me with this one act of being idea."

"I'll explain. Are you exactly the same now, today, as you were last year?"

"No, I have changed some."

"And next year will you be the same as you are now?"

"No. I hope to lose about ten pounds."

"You see; you are subject to change. What you are now, you weren't before and what you will be next is not what you are now. You don't exist in one act of being. Your existence is spread over time in successive moments of being. Accordingly, you cannot think every thought you will ever think all in one act."

"True. I think my brain would explode. I have enough trouble keeping clear on what I'm supposed to be doing today, much less what I am going to be doing forever."

"But the Most High cannot be limited by time, even three dimensional time. He is all that he is in one act, in one point in time, in an eternally present now. He doesn't change. He is what he is, or, as it says in the scriptures, 'I am I am.' He only exists in the eternal present tense, a point in time that contains all time. Let's go back to the time line. I'll explain how the Most High relates to it. First we expanded it and made it infinite in both directions. Then we expanded it again and made it possible to remain in one given moment of time but touring the universe, as it were, checking in on everything that is happening at that given moment. Now what we must do is take all of this three-dimensional time and collapse it into a point. This becomes the eternal present. All time is contained in that point. It is one point in time. All that is, was or will be exists in that point, and that is the dimension of time for the Most High."

"One act of being?" I said. "The infinitely big contained in the infinitely small."

"As it were, yes."

"But I don't follow why there is no change for God. I have heard people say that time is the measure of change but I don't understand that."

"Let's go back to the idea that the present is short, only a point in time. This is true for you as well as the

222

Most High. The present moment is infinitely short and has no dimensions. Accordingly, in the infinitesimal present there is no time for anything to change. Everything is stable. Only in the course of time can things change. When time stands still nothing changes."

"Let me try it." I said. "Let's stop time. Now, from this point of view, any event either has happened or is about to happen. Nothing changes when time stops."

"Exactly."

"So, because God exists in a moment or a point of time which never changes nothing can change in that perspective."

"Yes. The Most High exists in an eternally present moment. He has only one act of being. It is not succeeded by another one. If it were, then he would exist in time and he too would change."

"Therefore, in the eternal now, God exists in one act of being, unchanging, ruling over an ever changing universe. It is obvious, once you see it. He can know everything all at once. He can love everything at once. He possesses all virtue at once. He can be in all things fully at every moment they experience while for him it is only one moment. He will not change nor diminish. For him there is no past or future, no up or down or across. There is only the 'eternal now' for God."

"How does the bible begin?" Michael again seemed to abruptly change the subject. In the end he was simply explaining omnipresence from another angle.

"'In the beginning God created the heavens and the earth.'" I answered with certainty.

"Stop. You have gone too far."

"What?"

"Let's just deal with the phrase 'In the beginning God.' In the beginning there was only the Most High. There was nothing else—the Trinity, the Father, Son and Holy Spirit, one God in three persons—nothing more, nothing less. No heavens, no earth, no universe, no time, nothing—he was all there was. Within his one act of being, in his moment of time, time, as you know it, began. Now, what was the next word?"

"Created. 'In the beginning God created.'"

"Yes. The Most High created everything—all that is seen and unseen. So where did it all come from?"

"From God."

"Yes. It was not that the Most High took something that already was and then gave it form. He did not just form creation; he created it. Also, he created it from within himself, within his one act of being, right?"

"He had to. There wasn't anything else."

"So all that is simply came from within the Most High. In this sense, everything that has been created was originally in him, including you. Now put that in the present tense."

"So we should not say, 'everything that has been created, was originally in him.' Instead we should say 'Everything that is created, is still in him.'"

"Yes. It still is in him, still in his one act of being. As Paul said, 'In him we live and move and have our being.' There is nothing that is, that is not in the Most High. There is nothing which he does not encompass."

"From this perspective it would appear that I have understood omnipresence backwards. Omnipresence doesn't mean that the Most High is in every tree, but that every tree is in the Most High. The creator of all things, because he created all things in himself or from himself, by definition, must be omnipresent, or present to all things because all things are in him."

"Well done. Now, let's illustrate something similar mathematically. How good are your maths?"

"I think I need a cup of coffee!" I said as I got up. I also thought, "I could use another brain, Einstein's for instance." I got my coffee and said, "Go ahead. It has been over twenty years since I looked at a mathematics textbook, so go slow."

Michael took out a pen and began to write on a napkin, saying: "This symbol designates infinity." Michael wrote α. "In this equation it will represent the Most High. The number 'one' represents you, and '20b' will represent the rest of humanity's twenty billion people. Now solve this equation for me: Infinity minus one equals what?"

On the napkin Michael wrote $\alpha - 1 = ?$ I answered, "Infinity."

"Now try this one. Infinity minus twenty billion?" He wrote $\alpha - 20b = ?$

I answered, "It's still infinity."

"Correct. Now let's change it. Infinity plus one equals what?" On the napkin Michael wrote $\alpha + 1 = ?$

I answered, "Infinity."

"And this, infinity plus twenty billion?" He wrote $\alpha + 20b = ?$

I answered, "It's still infinity."

"The point I am making so far is about our importance relative to the Most High. He is infinite. We neither add nor subtract from his nature at all. Our existence, mathematically speaking makes no difference. Now, for the next point. What is infinity minus zero?"

"Infinity."

"Let's put that together with the previous equation."

Now I wrote: $\alpha - 20,000,000,000 = \alpha$ and then wrote $\alpha - 0 = \alpha$.

Michael said, "Since both are equal to α then $\alpha - 20,000,000,000 = \alpha - 0$. Now, subtract infinity from each side."

"$20,000,000,000 = 0$. Hold it! There must be something wrong!"

"Yes there is. Subtracting infinity is the problem, but it illustrates a point. Apart from the Most High, everything would be nothing."

The Trinity

Michael paused for a moment.

"OK," I said, "Here is a numbers question for *you*. How can three equal one?"

"Are you asking a mathematics question or a theological question?"

"Which one is harder to answer?"

"Neither is hard for me to answer."

"Which one will I have a hope of understanding?"

"The mathematical one is simple. Just count in a base that has one-third as its unit. Then three thirds would be written using the number one."

"OK, let's try the theological question. That was my real question anyway. The Trinity. Why three persons in one God? Why not three roles or even three gods who got along with each other? It would sure be easier to understand." I picked up my coffee and sat back, expecting that the coming explanation might take a while.

"A god who is easy to understand," Michael began, "would not hold your attention very long. In some ways it is like good poetry. The poems which begin, 'Roses are red, violets are blue…' are simple to write and shallow."

"That's true." I added, finishing the rhyme. "An hour of meditating on them is a waste of fifty-nine minutes."

"Such poems have no depth. A good poem will capture your attention quickly and also have such depth that you will desire to return to it over and over again and never tire of reading it. This is the nature of the Most High. He is beautiful in his simplicity and mysterious in his depth. The Trinity can be understood as simply as a shamrock or it can be contemplated throughout all eternity and still remain a mystery. The moment you understand the Trinity better is the moment you realise that this mystery is even more unfathomable than before. The full mystery of the nature of the Trinity is far beyond any creature's ability to comprehend."

"Could you help me comprehend it just a bit better?" I asked.

"Would you mind passing me your coffee?"

I was only slightly surprised. I assumed he did not desire it for its flavour nor need it for its caffeine. (I assume that angels don't get tired, although we never actually discussed this. Even if they did, I doubt caffeine would help keep them stay awake.) I passed him the cup. He set it directly in front of him and then looked around the room apparently checking if anyone was watching us. No one was. He put his right hand around the rim of the cup and his left around the bottom. Then he pulled to the right with his right hand and to the left with his left. I expected the cup to fall over. Instead, there were suddenly three cups, one in each hand, and the original standing alone in between. I sat, silent, staring.

"A lesson on the Trinity," he said. "Go ahead, try them."

I took a sip from each cup. They tasted exactly the same.

"Are they the same?"

"The last one needs more sugar." I said. Michael didn't laugh, so I added, "No, they are the same."

"Are they?"

I backtracked. "They, uhm, taste the same?" Hoping I'd guessed right.

"You are correct. They taste the same, absolutely, exactly the same. Down to the finest possible measurement you would find them the same, but are they exactly the same?"

"It depends on what you mean. If you are asking, are they comprised of the same substances: coffee suspended in water. I suppose the answer is yes. If you are asking are the molecules in the one cup identical to the ones in the other, I would say no. They can't be in two places at the same time."

"Take another sip from the first cup."

I did as I was told.

"Now look at the other two cups."

I did as I was told, again. The last two cups, although I had not touched them, had gone down in volume by the same amount as the first.

"In your frame of reference one thing cannot be in two places at the same time. In mine they can. In the frame of reference of the Most High, time and space provide no restrictions. You must keep that in mind to understand the Trinity. When you drink from the Father, you also drink from the Son and the Holy Spirit."

Michael rejoined the three cups as effortlessly as he had separated them, and then repeated his original action. Again there were three cups. This time, however, when I drank from them the first was ordinary black coffee, the second tasted like there was cream in it, although it looked black, the same as the first. The third was black with sugar. Yet, when I drank from one of them, the same phenomenon occurred. The volume in all three cups went down with each sip.

"Are they the same?" Michael asked.

"Well, they are all coffee, made from the same cup but they taste different."

"And when you drank from one, what happened to the others?"

"They still went down, just like before."

"So they are the same cup of coffee, but they appear to be in three different places at once and taste differently as well."

"Yes, meaning the Trinity is one and three at the same time."

"Yes."

"That is an improvement on the shamrock but I suspect I cannot recreate this in my own living room."

"Unfortunately not."

"Could you explain how you did that?"

"Later, if we have the time. Let me note, however, that any analogy to the Trinity is only that, an analogy. There is no accurate way to explain the Trinity by example because the Trinity is a singularity. There is only one in all that is. You can compare an apple with another apple or a chair with a chair. You cannot compare the Trinity with another Trinity. There is only one."

Michael handed a reunited cup back to me. I took another drink, wondering whether it would taste of cream and sugar.

"Would you like a shot at running the universe?"

I nearly spit out my coffee. "You can't be serious," I answered, slouching into the seat, "I have trouble running a tour for more than ten people for a week!"

"True enough. Let's make it simpler. How about if we made you responsible for that cup of coffee for ten minutes."

"Now that, I think I can handle!" I sat up again and looked around the restaurant. I didn't see anyone who looked suspicious. I sensed no unusual spiritual activity, other than Michael of course. "Yup. I think I can do it."

"Can you?"

By now I had learned the telltale signs of having spoken too soon. I scratched my head and said, "Probably not."

"If we remove the difficulty of having to hold the cup and its contents in being, then you would only need to keep the molecules, atoms and sub atomic particles relating to one another according to all the laws of the universe."

"But I don't know all the laws of the universe!"

"Nor does, nor can, any other human being. Still, let me show you what is involved. How many molecules do you think are in that cup?"

"Millions?"

"More."

"How much more?"

"A one with twenty-five zeros after it would get you close."

"So trillions of trillions," I said, picking something that sounded like a large number.

"You need work on your maths, but that is not the point. The point is that in this cup alone there a far more molecules than you could even count in your life-time, much less could you know where they all are in any given moment. However, even that is known by the Most High."

"…And I thought I was busy!" I said. "What a job description. Only God could keep track of everything. Now I see what occupies him."

"Is that what you think keeps him occupied?"

I quickly realised that God could not have keeping molecules doing what they are supposed to be doing as his main occupation in life. "No," I answered, "I suppose he is more interested in caring for the human race."

"That is true, however, that still isn't his primary occupation. It cannot be. Running a finite universe and caring for a few billion people are not sufficient objects for his infinite knowledge nor his infinite love."

Michael Shaughnessy

"Then what is?"

"You have now reached the key to understanding the Trinity."

"I have? I thought we had finished with the Trinity."

"We have hardly started."

"So what keeps God occupied? What holds his attention if not this universe?" Again a question occurred to me that would get me a Nobel Prize in physics if I had the answer, "Are there other universes? Other forms of life?" As one might expect, my question was not relevant to the point and received no helpful answer.

"The Most High is infinite in his capacity to know and love. Other universes or forms of life, no matter how vast, cannot do it. What can occupy his attention?"

"Something infinite, but surely, God doesn't just sit there and think about infinity! What could be worse than working on an infinite math equation forever! That sounds more like hell than heaven."

"No, the Father doesn't work on an infinite math problem or an infinite crossword puzzle just to keep his mind occupied."

"So what does he do?"

"He knows and loves the equally infinite Son...I am going to use a literary analogy to describe the Trinity." Michael continued. "It is one of the more effective ways to explain why the Trinity has to be just as it is. Why there must be three and only three persons in the one true God. It is the analogy used in the fourth gospel."

"I'm all ears." I said. "I wish I was all brain." I thought.

In the fourth gospel John speaks of the relationship between the Father and the Son. He calls the Son the 'Logos' in Greek or 'the Word' in English. The Word of the Father is not a spoken word as we are speaking now because the Word exists outside time and space limitations. The Word is really the thought of the Father. It is the thought of the thinker. Now, because the Father has his existence in one act of being, all that he thinks, he thinks in this one act. All that he knows, he knows at once. What is it that he knows? Not just what day you were born and where everything in the universe is located. This is all finite. One of the things the Father knows perfectly is himself, the infinite being. The main substance of his one thought in his one act of being is therefore infinite and perfect. This thought is called the Word of the Father, the Logos. Does that make sense?"

"I think so. The Father is all knowing. He exists in one act of being. His one thought in this one act includes all that is, including his own self-awareness."

"Yes. What occupies his mind is this one perfect yet infinite thought. Now, for the critical point. Because the Father is infinite, perfect and lacking in nothing, his thought is also infinite, perfect and lacking in nothing. In other words, the thought of the Father, or the Word of the Father, is the perfect and total reflection of the Father. The thought or Word possesses all and exactly the attributes of the Father. The Father is a person. Therefore the thought also must be a person. The thinker is divine in his nature, so the thought, in order to be perfect, must be divine in its nature. Thus the Father begets or produces the Son who is of the exact same nature as the Father. He also would not exist without the Father, just as the thought does not exist without the thinker. Yet, they are one in being. They exist together in the one act of being. However, just as the thinker is not the thought and the thought is not the thinker, so the Father is not the Son, nor is the Son the Father. The have the same nature but are distinguishable from one another."

"And because the Son is an infinite and divine person the thing that occupies him is the other infinite and divine person, the Father."

"Yes, the occupation of the infinite Father is knowing and loving the infinite Son. The occupation of the infinite Son is knowing and loving the infinite Father."

"What about the Spirit? Why is it necessary that the Spirit exist? I would have thought from this that the Father and the Son are enough for each other."

"I must continue the literary analogy. I said the Son is the thought of the Father, or the thought of the thinker. If one constructs a simple sentence the Trinity gets reflected in that sentence. The sentence is, 'The thinker thinks the thought.' There are three elements to the sentence: the subject, the object and the verb. The perfect thinker, perfectly thinks, the perfect thought. Not only is the thought a perfect reflection of the thinker, but the act of thinking itself must also be complete and perfect.

"Now I will change it slightly, substituting love for think, because, as it is written in the First Letter of John, 'God is love.' The Father loves the Son. This love is the Holy Spirit. The perfect lover, perfectly loves, the perfect beloved. Now, if the love that the Father and the Son have for each other is to be perfect and complete in one act of being, this act of love must be infinite and personal as well. Nothing can be lacking in the way that the Father and the Son love one another. Thus the act of love, the Holy Spirit, must be of the exact same nature as the Father and the Son. The Spirit is also a person who would not exist without the Father and the Son but must exist if the Father and Son exist."

"So the Father and the Son exist in the unity of the Holy Spirit. The lover and the beloved are united by the love that exists between them. The lover loves the beloved."

"Exactly. They are one in being. They have the exact same nature, but they are different persons."

"That explains why there are three persons in the one infinite God. Why can't there be four or an infinite number? For example, why isn't the third person the Father's love for the Son and the fourth person the Son's love for the Father?"

"Put in simple terms it is because they would be the same person. The Father's love for the Son is exactly the same as the Son's love for the Father. There can be no difference. It is one and the same Holy Spirit. Or put slightly different, the Father thinks only one thought; the Son also thinks only one thought. This thought is one and the same. It is the Spirit. There is no other thought to be thought. It is one, perfect and complete."

The Physics of Angels

"Michael," I continued, "this is helpful for understanding the nature of God, but what about the nature of angels? You too are immaterial. You too seem to be able to function in various dimensions of time and space. Yet, there are differences between angels and God. Can you explain them?"

"The easiest place to start is that I too am a created being. I owe my existence to the Most High. The existence that I have is received. I can take this form you see today only because that ability has been given to me."

"But you seem to be able to move anywhere in space and time that you choose. Does that mean you too could be omnipresent?"

"Not exactly. Although I am not bound by the same time and space restrictions as you, I am still bound. I can live in the present moment for an eternity, but I cannot visit the future and I cannot affect the past. The right to affect a point in time belongs only to those living in that time, never to those visiting it."

"But could you not visit every point in space in a given point in time from the past or present?"

"In theory, possibly, but in fact, no."

"Could you explain please?"

"Because I am not omniscient, I don't know where everything is so as to go visit it. Second, I am an angel whose every act is to glorify the Most High. I only do as he says. He has not ordered me to go and visit all that is."

"Michael," I interjected quickly, not wanting to stop yet changing the subject slightly, "are there any ways to describe or to measure the spiritual world and its interaction with the material world?"

"Yes."

"So can you tell me how a spiritual being like you can take on a material shape like you have?"

"As I noted before, the interaction between energy and matter is a delicate balance. Angels have been given the ability to affect that balance and turn energy into matter. That is what I am doing. It is, however, unnatural for me. My preference is to be a spiritual being only, not a mixture of matter and spirit as humans are. In the age to come, you too will have this power, just as Jesus had it naturally in his resurrected body."

"I'm not a physicist, but are there laws which determine how that works?"

"Yes. Let's start with the speed of light. What do you know about it?"

"It's fast. Isn't it 186,000 miles per second?"

"That isn't the key point."

"Then how about 'nothing can go faster than the speed of light?'"

"That is exactly the mistaken notion I was looking for. Moving faster than the speed of light is an issue in this time space world. Angels aren't bound by the laws of matter. Indeed, we can travel faster than the speed of light. Now if you take that fact and combine it with the formula for the mathematical resolution of the four forces in the universe, and make some corrections in Einstein's theory of relativity and some revisions in current thinking regarding quantum mechanics, which I can show you, and then make some correct applications using imaginary numbers and what happens when you divide a number by zero in the non-material universe the interrelationship between the spiritual world and the material world becomes much simpler."

"Wait a minute. I said, 'slow.' Besides, the last I heard, you still can't divide a number by zero."

"What is impossible with man is possible with…"

"Nope, nope, nope…hold it. I wanted a mathematical explanation, not a theological one. Michael, could you just write up the mathematics for me?"

"Have you ever seen the Einstein's derivation of $E=MC2$?"

"Yes, why?"

"It takes a good bit of time to write it out. The same is true with regard to the derivation of the key law of quantum mechanics. Now, in order to reconcile those two theories, plus the four forces of the universe, as you call them, would take time we don't have. Even though that would be child's play relative to some of the mathematical formulas governing the spiritual world, which are also based on a system of numbers substantially more complicated than your imaginary numbers system. All in all it would take too much time to explain how and why it works."

"Especially if you expect me to understand it. How about if I ask you some more simple questions?"

"Go ahead."

"Good. It is about space and matter. There was a big debate in the Middle Ages on this. The question is, 'How many angels can dance on the head of a pin?'"

"All of us or none of us. Take your pick. We are immaterial beings. We are without measure. An infinite number of angels could dance on the head of a pin, except there aren't an infinite number of angels."

"And none of us?"

"None of us, because without bodies it is difficult to see how you would describe anything we do as dancing. I could also answer, 'none of us,' because the Most High would not likely command such trivial behaviour from his primary messengers and servants."

"That makes sense. Now, how did you do that bit with my coffee?"

"It again has to do with the control of matter. On this assignment I have been given the ability to make molecules do as I will, therefore it was no problem to have the molecules, which comprised your cup, move in such a pattern that there appeared to be three cups simultaneously. In fact, each cup was in existence only one third of the time. The other two thirds it appeared as each of the other two cups. Because they were moving at nearly the speed of light your eye could not perceive it as anything but three cups."

"But when I drank the coffee it didn't feel like only one third of what it should."

"I didn't say that I divided everything into thirds. The cup from which you drank had all the molecules but only for a third of the time. Once you drank them they were out of the three cups and into you. That is why the level went down in all three."

"OK, next question. In your present form are you limited to normal human functions?"

"I mainly appear to be human. I am not. I could walk through a wall. I will not grow hungry and tired. I am not an angel incarnate. I am energy turned to matter under the control of my angelic powers. In my capacity to think, I remain Michael the Archangel. My ability to think is not a function of a human brain. It is that of an angel."

"Nice trick, I wish I could do it."

"No, you wouldn't, and even in heaven, when you could, you wouldn't."

"Did I understand you correctly before and now again that human beings, in heaven, will be able to materialise and dematerialise at will?"

"Able to, yes, want to, no."

"Why? Or Why not?"

"For the same reason that although I can take on material form, I prefer not to do so. The Most High created me to be an angel, a specific one named Michael. I have no desire to be anything other than what the Most High created me to be. I do not envy human beings even though they are created in the image and likeness of the Most High himself. Human beings in heaven will only want to be exactly what they were created by the Most High to be. They won't want to be angels; they won't even want to be the Most High and they certain won't want to be any other human being than the one they are. When you are constantly being satisfied, you do not seek a substantial change. In that day you will finally be content with who you are. You will be at peace internally. Your sole desire will be to know the Most High more deeply, love him more fully and serve him more totally."

The Incarnation

"I have another question."

"You have far more than one, but go ahead and ask."

"I assume you understand the Incarnation better due to your current physical form."

"In some minor ways yes."

"Can you explain it?"

"The Incarnation?"

"Yes."

"No."

"No? That surprises me."

"It shouldn't. Only the Three in One can truly understand how the Son is fully human and fully divine."

I began to wonder about Michael's theological training, so I asked, "Haven't you read the statement from the Council of Chalcedon on this?"

"The Council statement reasonably defines the truth, but the truth defined is not the truth understood. You can define infinity, you cannot really understand it."

"Let me try again. Can you help me understand the Incarnation better?"

"Possibly, however you are in a better position than I to understand the Incarnation."

Needless to say, I was astounded. Until now there had been no question of who was the teacher and who was the pupil. "How can this be?" I asked.

"You are an incarnate being yourself. I am not."

"What?"

"I am purely spirit. When I take human form I am not human, no matter how hard I try. I remain a spirit who is simply activating matter in a way sensible to you. You, on the other hand, are a spiritual being as well as a physical being, spirit and body."

"A combination of a little less than an angel and a little more than an animal in one being?"

"No. You are also more than angel and more than animal."

"Help me again. I need that explained."

"First, you are right, you are more than an animal. Animals do not have the capacity to reason and are not self-aware. This is not something they can evolve into. This belongs to the nature of spiritual beings only."

"That part is clear."

"Second, you are more than an angel, not less. You are a spiritual being integrally joined to matter."

"But I don't see the advantage. It seems to me that you have the advantage in your mastery over time, space and matter. How are we more than angels?"

"There are numerous reasons. First, consider the fact of your senses. You have the advantage of seeing, tasting, hearing, feeling, smelling. We do not know these things. What is even more important is that in the life to come you will have a resurrected body, one no longer limited in your current fashion. In the resurrection your spirit will be fully master of your body. You will have the freedom of angels and the sensory capacity of humans."

That did sound like an advantage.

"Secondly, consider emotion. You are created with the capacity to feel. You love, you fear, you rejoice, you mourn."

"Is this not true of the angels?"

"Not in the same way. We have no bodies, which are moved by passion. Our passions are at best what you might call cool. They are intellectual passions. You can be moved to tears. I cannot. I can understand loss, but I do not feel it. I can calculate the risks and be uncertain of an outcome. I cannot shudder with fear. I love the Most High, but it is admiration, not passion. It is intellectual awe and wonder, an impulse to understand the infinite. It is not a hunger to be joined to Him. It is not a physical, emotional yearning to be completed only in union, like the bride and the bridegroom. A human being in the state for which it was created has all these things working together, his intellect, his will, his passions and his body."

"It would appear that human beings have passions which are neither angelic nor animal."

"Yes, exactly. They are purely human. Consider human love. Is it more than two animals procreating?"

"It certainly should be."

"Yes. It is also more than the love that I have for others."

"How do you mean?"

"Physical love is at the centre of what it means to be human. It is in this act that two become one. Human love is more than angelic love plus animal bodies. It is not just profound intellectual admiration plus copulation. It is the joining of life to life. It is the integration of two lives mentally, emotionally, and physically. Even their wills grow to be one. But this does not explain how fully set apart and unique human beings are. There is something else which is even more profound about human love and sets it above the angels'."

"That is…"

"That is the ability to participate in the creation of a new spiritual being, a new human being. The Most High, in his wisdom has put it into the nature of human beings to procreate. With every act of conception there is a co-operation between the Most High and the two humans involved. They pass on the life he has given them, just as all animals propagate according to their own nature, however, the Most High also participates by providing the spiritual nature, the eternal soul, for each person who is conceived. We angels do not have the privilege of working with the Most High in procreating other spiritual beings. Only humans have that privilege. You are in the image and likeness of the Most High in a way that even we are not; you are creators of spiritual life. We are obedient servants. We accomplish but we don't create. This was at the heart of Lucifer's envy. He desired to create, but in the end he only had the capacity to destroy."

"Your description of human beings almost makes us seem superior to God because he has no body, no emotions. Can you explain that?"

"Yes. You are most certainly not superior to the Most High, just as, in certain areas, you are not and will not be superior to angels. To answer your question however, the Most High knew what he was creating in creating the human race. Although he had no body, he knew what it is to have a body. It is from this part of his infinite wisdom that he was able to create such an intricate creature such as you are. You should also call to mind the subject of our current discussion, the

Incarnation. In a manner of speaking, the Most High does have a body, that of the Son Incarnate, Jesus Christ."

"I want to come back to that issue, the physical body of Jesus Christ. First, however, let me note that your description of spiritual beings makes them sound like disembodied brains, pure intellect, but surely they are more than that?"

"Yes. Although the intellect is the easiest to describe concretely, there is something much more fundamental to every spiritual being. It is most easily termed identity. It is who you are."

"At the risk of wearing out these words, can you explain?"

"Certainly." Michael proceeded to produce a picture from 1970. It was not one of my most flattering portraits, but then flattering portraits aren't my strong suit. "Do you recognise this?" He asked.

"Unfortunately, yes."

"Who is it?"

"I must admit; it is I."

"In what way do you mean that? Is it the same body?"

"Definitely not. I was just skin and bones then. Even more, I do know that our bodies change all their cells in the course of seven years, or something like that. There probably isn't one molecule of the 'me' of 1970 left in my current body."

"Therefore who you are is not fundamentally your material make-up. How about your emotions?"

"They are even more fleeting."

"True. How you feel is not who you are. How about your thoughts?"

245

"They too flee, one after the other, yet somehow I do remember and retain a lot of them somewhere in my mind."

"Yes. Though your thoughts are not fundamentally you, they and the ability to store them have something to do with your identity. However, even that is not you."

"Why?"

"Have you ever seen anyone in a coma?"

"Yes, my father before he died."

"How much self awareness did he have?"

"None from what I could tell and what doctors seemed to say."

"Yet you still identified him as your father."

"Absolutely."

"In a diminished state?"

"Yes, maybe, but still unquestionably my father."

"So even your awareness of your identity is not essential to your identity."

"I guess not."

"So you can say, 'I am myself,' but you cannot locate this identity particularly."

"True."

"This is also true for angels. Being less complicated beings there are fewer places to look for the seat of identity. Still, it is no easier to find in me than in you, but let's not give up just yet. When your father died, what happened to him?"

"I assume and hope he is with the Lord."

"And how would he be with the Lord? Physically, in a body?"

"I presume not. Best I can tell, the resurrection of the dead has not yet happened."

"How about the rest?"

"I would guess that he is self aware, that he thinks. I don't know about emotions. Physically sensation must also be somehow lacking."

"Given all that, how would you describe your father now?"

"He is. He is spiritually alive but physically dead."

"In the death of human beings, their identity goes with them in their spirit, not their body. However they are in fact diminished because they are not all they used to be, nor are they all they will be. To be human is to be matter and spirit, body and soul. In the resurrection from the dead, all human beings will be re-united: spirit with matter."

"So what does all this have to do with the Incarnation?"

"It is meant to show you that it is possible to be one being with parts. Every human being is only, fully, what he or she is when both the physical and the spiritual nature are present. Your sense of identity encompasses both, and without them both you are not fully, really, who you are. At the heart of the mystery of the Incarnation is this same question of identity. Who is Jesus Christ, Son of God, Son of Man? In terms of who he is as the Son of God, the Second Person of the Trinity, this identity is divine and eternal as explained earlier. In terms of who he is as Jesus, son of Mary, this identity is fully human, and as such it was a self-awareness that grew and an identity that became understood although it existed from the moment of conception. The Incarnate Son of God is one person, one identity, with a divine and human nature that are inseparably one in Jesus Christ."

"Now," I continued, "that is all very helpful, but here is my real question. It goes back to all of what we were previously talking about. Where is the physical body of Jesus now? Is he in a heaven that is some cordoned-off section of the universe about which we know nothing as yet, other than that is where he dwells bodily? Or is he, in some molecular way, distributed through the entire universe? Is he dwelling on earth secretly as a lost child in a park, a homeless man on the street, the unnamed and unknown whom we are to love and serve as Christ himself? Or is he even closer due to his authority over time, space and matter and thus is in the other person in my presence who should be loved and served right now, for he or she is Christ?"

"You have learned something…"

I didn't bother to ask him what.

"When the Logos became incarnate, that is, when he took on human flesh, he joined himself to your nature forever, not just for thirty some years. When he died and rose, he did so as a human being. He has not put off that nature in heaven; he remains the God-Man, the incarnate Son. To explain where he is I will begin with explaining heaven."

"A good place to start, I should think."

"Except that literally speaking, it is no place to start. Heaven is not a physical place. There is no *place* where you can locate it. Heaven is the presence of the Most High. One would more accurately describe those experiencing eternal happiness already as being 'present to' heaven than 'in' it."

"Well, then does heaven really exist?"

"Does joy exist?"

"Yes, I have experienced it."

"So, lets go there."

"Where?"

"To the place where joy is."

"It doesn't exist in a place. You can't *go there*...Oh, now I get it." I was a bit slow but it was suddenly clear. "Some things exist but have no material dimension and therefore no location."

"Exactly."

"Heaven."

"Heaven is more like joy than like Tallahassee."

(I've never been to Tallahassee, but I would guess it isn't heaven on earth.)

Michael continued. "It has more in common with an experience than with a physical location."

"That is a helpful start."

"But it does not address your key question, which is a physical one."

"Yes. Where are the molecules of Jesus' body?"

"Your question, while valid, expects that the laws of eternity, infinity, and heaven are the same as the laws of earth or this temporal universe. They aren't. Jesus Christ is the first born of the *new creation*."

"And," I interrupted, "Christ's body, as part of the new creation does not follow the laws of the old creation universe."

"Yes, matter and time and energy are bound together according to very specific laws in the earthly frame of reference. These same laws simply do not hold true in the heavenly frame of reference nor in the new-creation frame of reference."

"And whatever the frame of reference for the risen Lord is, it is not the old earthly one."

"Correct. You first have to understand how the new creation exists both spiritually and materially before you can even begin to answer any question about space and time."

"So space and time will exist in heaven."

"Yes but in a way completely different than they do here."

"Michael, one more question?"

"OK."

"Is it possible to prove the existence of God?"

"Absolutely. That is the one thing that will eventually be proven beyond any doubt. There are no atheists on the other side of the grave."

"How about now?"

"Even now there are few true atheists. Satan most certainly isn't!"

"I suppose not. It doesn't make much sense to fight a non-existent enemy."

"No. But a real one in a battle that dwarfs all others demands constant attention." Michael rose to leave, saying, "I must get back to work!"

"Are we done?" I asked.

"Yes, except for one last thing." He replied. "Throughout the course of our conversations you have sought to prise some bit of information that would allow you some 'corner on a market.'"

I knew better than to look surprised.

"I will give you one tip and one tip only. Don't bet on the Vikings in the superbowl next year."

With that, Michael looked around the room and in an instant, vanished. My lunch at McDonald's, my lessons in physics, and the visitations of the Archangel of Westminster were finished.

ABOUT THE AUTHOR

Michael Shaughnessy is a member of the Servants of the Word, a religious order including men from both Protestant and Catholic backgrounds. They live a common and celibate life. Their work involves the evangelisation of youth, the advancement of Christian Unity and the promotion of Christian community. Michael Shaughnessy is involved in youth work in the USA (Christian Youth Challenge) and in Belfast, Northern Ireland (Youth Initiatives). He has served as Ecumenical Officer in Westminster under Cardinals Basil Hume and Cormac Murphy-O'Connor. He has written other works including <u>A Concise Catholic Catechism</u>. (Available from <u>amazon.co.uk</u>.)

Printed in the United States
1066500003B/1-57